Cont‹

Editor's Introduction

Dr. Darran McCann

Convenor of the M.A. in Creative Writing

This centre holds, and spreads.

So wrote Seamus Heaney in his great 1975 poem, *Kinship*. The line has become an unofficial motto for the Centre for creative writing at Queen's University Belfast that bears his name. It was Heaney's direct call-back – and riposte – to Yeats, from half a century prior: 'Things fall apart, the centre cannot hold. Mere anarchy is loosed upon the world.'

Dr. Darran McCann

You'd have been forgiven in the Belfast of 1975 for thinking the centre had given, that things had fallen apart, that anarchy had been loosed. Perhaps in the world of 2016 you'd be forgiven for thinking the same.

The centre cannot hold?

This collection of work from recent graduates of the Seamus Heaney Centre is our riposte: *This* centre holds, and spreads.

Every work of creation is an act of generosity by the artist, a gift to the world given with scant hope that it will be received with nearly so much generosity in return. In your hands you hold a collection of fiction, drama and poetry generously and graciously given to you, the reader, by the Seamus Heaney Centre's Classes of 2014 and 2015. *Blackbird* is the first such formal anthology of work by SHC graduates, Volume 1 of what will be a biennial series. Future MA students will have their chance to appear in Volume 2, Volume 3 and beyond, and the series will run for as long as we're still here, nurturing and bringing forth the potential of new writers as they find their voices. If we're all very lucky, that will be far into the distant future.

Blackbird contains work by writers from the north and south of Ireland, from England and from across the Atlantic. The work collected here is remarkable in its range of genres and the breadth of thematic concerns. Here are tales of feral youth, of sexual transgression, of the frustrations of small-town life and of facing up to mortality. Settings range from the historical to the contemporary to the futuristic. From the imagined future of a post-apocalyptic Ireland, to the all-too-real past of post-apocalyptic Chernoybl. From pre-revolutionary Russia to post-Troubles Belfast. From the grittily realistic to the magic realist. These are writers who have excelled in the the intensive, structured and collegial setting of the Seamus Heaney Centre, where they have experimented, exchanged ideas and confidences, and learned nuts-and-bolts editorial skills that will serve them for the rest of their careers. This is work to be relished for its originality, for its sophistication and for its aplomb.

The challenge for you, dear reader, is to exercise your own judgment about the work before you. With new writers, there are no received opinions or established reputations for the reader to fall back on. Can you recognize fresh talent when you see it? It has been a privilege for myself, Prof. Sinéad Morrissey, Dr Garrett Carr, Dr Jimmy McAleavey, Dr Tim Loane, Dr Leontia Flynn and Prof. Fran Brearton to work with these writers, and it will be our pleasure to observe their progress in the years ahead. In most cases these are writers are being published in book form for the first time – in most cases, I confidently predict it won't be the last. Their names are listed in the Contents page: check back in ten or twenty years and see which of these names you have come to know well from the careers they've gone on to have.

The blackbird is the logo of The Seamus Heaney Centre, chosen by our founding Director and Chair of Poetry, Prof. Ciaran Carson. This is very much a Heaney Centre collection, and it testifies to how this Centre betters all who pass through it. (I speak with some authority here – Class of 2006.) But the work done in the unprepossessing corridors of 46-48 University Road does not end here. It ripples out in benign, civilizing waves into wider society, enriching even those who have never heard of the place, in ways they will never know but would miss if it was gone.

Hope was in short supply in the Belfast of 1975. Thank God, at least we had the poets. Heaney was still hopeful back then; but in 2012, close to the end of his life, he would write bleakly that it seemed as though the whole world had turned into 'one big Ulster now.'

He always did have a genius for seeing the universal in the parochial.

If the world of 2016 is one big Ulster now, and if the centre is to hold, we're going to need new voices. We're going to need to cultivate the creative genius of this city, this country and beyond.

Thank God then, for these new voices. And for the Seamus Heaney Centre. This Centre holds, and spreads.

DMcC, October 2016

The Red Forest

Elizabeth Byrne

Pasha Vasilyevich Ivanov, the last Liquidator, is finishing up with some tourists when I arrive at the hotel car park in Chista. I'm pleased that they look traumatised. As always, Pasha ends with his big joke.

'So, the American robot is on the roof for five minutes, and then it breaks down. The Japanese robot is on the roof for five minutes, and then breaks down. The Russian robot is up there two hours! Then a command comes in over the loudspeaker: 'Private Ivanov! In two hours, you're welcome to come down and have a cigarette break.''

He laughs, claps a shocked looking woman on the shoulder, and whips his dirty wool cap from his head for tips. It's cruel really, his pink scalp makes certain they'll give him some guilt money. I know for a fact that he shaves his head, but I say nothing. Tourists here are ghouls, he might as well profit. They drop notes and coins into his hands, and hurry off to their waiting coach. He's poking through the cash when I walk over.

'Tight fisted bastards'. He glares at me, then spits onto the ground. 'And now you, with your ludicrous ideas. Always a pain in the ass.'

'What can I say Pasha? You're the only man for the job.'

He holds out his hand for the money. I give him a roll of dollars which he starts to count immediately.

'Two-fifty now, three hundred when we get back. Don't you trust me? I'm offended.'

'Hmmph. Trusting women is never a good idea in my experience.'

He's right, this is a ludicrous idea. But I have to know the truth. Despite the regulations and my promise to my dying mother, today I'm going into the Red Forest.

Pasha folds the notes into the unimaginable recesses of his filthy coat, and gets into the car. I take out my radiation suit, pull the trousers on over my jeans, and zip up the top half over my thick sweater with some difficulty. I don't bother with the hood yet, and loop the straps of the mask around my wrist loosely, so it will be easy to grab. Finally I swap my shoes for plastic-covered boots and pull on gloves. Pasha watches me with amusement as I clamber into the car.

'It doesn't come with a matching purse? Oh, they've missed a trick there!'

Ignoring him I pick up the dosimeter and switch it on, and wait for the first ten seconds of high-pitched whine to settle into regular clicks.

'Ready now, are you? All safe and tucked up?'

'I just don't want any important parts shrivelling up if you get us lost.'

The grin drops from his face and he glares at me. He's refused my offer of protective gear, although he craftily suggested I could add the price of it to his fee. He was amazed when I agreed. No-one can say I didn't try to keep him safe.

As we drive off I look across the fields to my research lab and then further away to the Chernobyl plant itself. I can just make out the cover on Reactor 4, a sharper edge against the rounded domes of the other reactors. Twenty tons of nuclear fuel is still lying there in the ruined core, and nobody really knows what's happening with it. The core could be dead, or just sleeping, waiting patiently for its next opportunity. The concrete cover was intended to contain it forever. But not even thirty years have passed, and already it's crumbling. I've seen birds fly in and out of it. I wonder sometimes what kind of nest they've built in there, and what kind of eggs they lay.

The countryside we're passing through is green and beautiful. New visitors to the Zone, expecting an apocalyptic wasteland, are always surprised. We pass meadows of purple wildflowers and waist-high grass. The overgrown hedges almost conceal the lethal dose notices.

Pasha mutters under his breath in his native Belarusian, still annoyed with me. But as we get closer to the forest his curiosity gets the better of him.

'Tell me Professor, what do the other big brains back at the lab think of our little excursion?'

'They don't know about it. They're all up at the reactor.'

'Sticking plasters on the cracks are they? Ha! This is a not-so official trip? I knew it. So, we go into the Forest, you get some pictures and readings that no-one else has, and then what? You get some new post and a fat salary? You get out of the zone altogether? That's it, isn't it?'

'Not exactly, Pasha.'

We pass suddenly from daylight into gloom as we enter the forest. The outer trees are ugly pines, needles of dark green stabbing at each other. At first I can see out between their spindly trunks, but soon they grow closer together, blocking the light. The undergrowth is dense and twisted. Several times I think I see a flash of animal movement in the mirror, but look too late and only see swaying branches or shaking leaves. With one hand on the wheel, I pull my hood up over my head.

After a few miles we come to a fork in the road, partially blocked by the rusting remains of a checkpoint. Pasha points right. I steer around the twisted metal and drive down the track, and we're swallowed up in the deepest part of the wood. It's now or never.

'Pasha. When you knew my father, did he ever tell you where he was from?'

'Kovalenko? No. He didn't say much. Anyway I told you. Liquidators talked about women and football. That's it.'

I reach over and open the glove compartment, and take out the photograph.

'Remember this?'

He stares at it but doesn't take it from my hand. I put it on the dashboard. It shows a group of young men in a stairwell somewhere in the reactor, smiling wearily at the camera with arms around each other's shoulders. They're wearing a jumble of military uniforms and firefighter overalls, plastic goggles and paper surgical masks dangling round their necks. They're covered in dust and ash. No radiation suits. At the back there is one tall figure wearing misshapen home-made armour; panels of lead punched with holes and tied with string. He is holding a hatchet and wearing heavy leather gloves, and has a scarf wrapped round his face.

'That's you, isn't it?'

Pasha looks ahead, stony faced and silent.

'And that's my Dad at the front. See? Smiling away. He was dead a month later. They all were. It's a picture of twelve dead men. One survivor, Pasha. Just you...'

'So?' he barks.

'So what made you so fucking lucky?'

He looks at me with suspicion.

'If you wanted to whine about your dead Dad we could have just stayed in Chista and got drunk. What's this really about?'

Cunning old bastard.

'It's about Paryshev. That's where I want to go.'

He stares in disbelief.

'My father was born there. His mother lived there, my grandmother. Zinaida Yevdokimovna Kovalenka. And... I think you've been there too.'

Pasha twists in his seat and shouts at me, spittle flying from his lips.

'Paryshev? No way! You're crazy. Fucking crazy. Digging around about me were you? You have no right. Take me back. Now!'

'Listen, please? I think my grandmother might be alive. She wasn't that old in 1986. And you know that even after the evacuations, people came back. Especially old people. Look at Redkovka. Whole families still live there, people in their nineties who snuck back to their homes…'

Pasha has calmed down. Now he speaks as if trying to talk me down off a ledge.

'Paryshev is dead and empty. I saw it with my own eyes, there is no-one in that village, okay?'

'She could have come back. She could be there now. It happens. You know it does.'

He is silent.

'Please Pasha. Help me. I need to know if I'm the last survivor. The last Kovalenko.'

He looks at the photograph on the dashboard.

'If you won't help me, I'll just try to find it on my own.'

He growls, closes his eyes, turns his face away from me.

But after a few minutes he unbuttons his coat. There's a grimy bag of thick leather stitched into the lining. He opens it, and carefully takes out an old hatchet. It has a wooden handle, worn smooth, and the blade looks sharp. He holds it in his left hand, turning it so I can get a good look.

'It wasn't luck. Just so you know. I had this. I cut myself nice squares of lead. I was fast. I ran onto the roof fast, I did my job, I ran back off. I was faster than any of them.'

Pasha carefully lays the hatchet in his lap.

'I'll show you Paryshev. But I warned you.'

This strip of forest looks exactly like the rest to me, but Pasha is sure it's the right place. As soon as I stop he's out of the car, tucking his hatchet into his belt and setting off through the trees. He walks as if strolling along a well-lit avenue, not looking around or down at his feet. I pick my way carefully after him, peering through my mask to avoid tripping over the tangled undergrowth. The dosimeter clicks steadily.

Held straight in front of me it's high and fast, but I've heard worse. If I drop my arm, point it at the ground beneath us, the clicks become more rapid and urgent. Not a place to drop anything, definitely not a place to fall down. A ten-second scrabble in the earth here would be lethal.

'The village is just through there. Look.'

The ranks of living pine trees stop at a clearing of bare black earth. On the other side bright red leafless trees stretch dead branches into the sky, like gnawed but still bloody bones. Their trunks are ringed with bulbous growths, and their roots are knotted and exposed. The earth itself seems to have drawn away from such poisoned things.

He was right. It's an empty place.

Pasha walks straight over to a cottage and I follow him in. I turn the frantic dosimeter off. It's only repeating what I already know. The whole place is very, very hot. I look around the little room. Bare wood floor. Faded red curtains with a pattern of roses. A glass fronted cabinet, with a single blue patterned plate behind clouded panes. A dark wooden drop-leaf table with delicately carved edges. A calendar with an illustration of smiling Soviet children, perhaps still marking the May-day festival thirty years ago. A tiny bedroom off the kitchen, with an empty bed covered in a colourful knitted blanket. A layer of dust over every surface. We can stay for ten minutes, and that will be pushing it.

Pasha puts down his hatchet on the wooden table and picks up a dusty china cup. He turns it over, as though assessing its worth.

'I wouldn't touch anything', I warn him.

He gives me a sour look, and replaces the cup on the table with exaggerated care.

'You were here for the evacuation?'

'You already know I was.'

'And you think this was my grandmother's cottage?'

'Could be. Hard to tell what's what now. We ploughed most of Paryshev into the ground and buried it.'

He shrugs.

"Zinaida', you said?'

He looks around, shrugs again.

'There was one stubborn old woman who wouldn't leave. Shouted curses at us all, made a fuss. Almost made some of the boys cry, the things she said, that their own mothers would be ashamed of them for turning a poor old lady out of her home. Ha! She scared them more than the General!'

He wanders around the room as he speaks, peering into the cabinet, opening and closing cupboards, not looking at me.

'This was her house. She was a pain in the backside, maybe you inherited that from her?'

He grins. As always it isn't a pretty sight.

'What happened to her?'

'Nothing. We left her here. Hosed down the outside of the house to clear the dust. She shouted at us for trampling her sunflowers. Ha!'

'She just… stayed? What did she do when everyone was gone?'

'She had vegetables. I think she had a cow. What could we do?'

I stare around the empty cottage. My father might have eaten at that table, sat on that chair. He was long gone by 1986, living a good Soviet life as a firefighter, with his young wife and baby girl in a nice apartment in Pripyat. I wonder if we ever visited my grandmother here. I know we never came back after. Not once, my mother told me. She obeyed all the warnings, to keep me safe. So my grandmother would have had no-one. No neighbours. No electricity once the reactor failed, no heating or stove except an old fireplace. No radio. Almost nothing to show the cottage was not some relic from centuries ago. Nothing except the lethal radiation embedded in every atom of the place.

'Why did she stay here all alone?' I whisper.

Pasha considers me carefully.

'She wasn't alone. She had all the cats and dogs.'

'She had… what?"

'We came back to shoot them, you see, a couple of weeks later. Pets, you know? Left behind. She'd been feeding them, with what I don't know, milk and scraps. She came to the door when we arrived and I saw them all, in the garden, on the windowsills, in and around the house. Must have been twenty or thirty cats and dogs. They weren't even fighting. They were skinny, raggedy looking, all just weaving in and out, around her and the house. She looked right at me, your grandmother, saw the gun in my hand.'

Pasha moves over to the window now, and stares out at the red trees. It'll be dark soon, but the last of the sun casts some light onto his face.

'I look right at her, and I shout out to the boys, 'Comrades, we must spread out and hunt for cats and dogs! It is our duty to shoot them if we see them, to prevent them straying and spreading radiation!' One boy asked if I was mad, couldn't I see them all right in front of us? But the others understood. They were all scared of me anyway, because I wasn't dead yet. Not even sick. So, we all start calling out 'Here kitty! Here doggy!' as loud as we can and walk away from the house. We walk around for maybe ten minutes, and see nothing. Nothing. There aren't even birds singing. We get back to the truck. Your grandmother is standing in this doorway here, door closed behind her, staring at us. Not a single cat or a dog anywhere in sight. So I ask her, 'Old Mother, we have an important job to do here. Have you seen any cats or dogs in the village today?' And calm as you like she looks at me and says 'Son, not a single one. God bless you in your duty'. Not even a flicker in her face, as though we can't hear all the barking and scrabbling behind her in the house! Ha! So…I say 'God bless you too Mother'. And we leave.'

There are tears are running down my face behind my plastic mask.

'What happened to her?'

He stays still, staring out the window. I can't tell if he even hears me.

'I came back once or twice, left some food, some firewood. She didn't open the door, but I saw her peeping out the window and I waved at her. Then one day I come and the door is open. I walk in, calling out for her. The place is empty, but there's ashes in the grate, dishes on the table. The chair on its side on the floor… I picked it up. Cleaned up a little. I waited. But there were no cats, no dogs, not a living thing left.'

It's dark outside now. His face is entirely in shadow. I feel cold, and suddenly remember cold is not the problem, that we've been here far too long. I take a last look around and walk over to him.

'Thank you. You tried to help her.'

I put my hand on his arm, gently.

'We can go now Pasha. We need to get away from here and get back to the car.'

'Too late', he says softly, pointing out the window.

In the garden in front of the cottage, the wolves of the forest have come.

Their coats are thin and black, and their eyes are yellow. They make no sound. They are impatient. They are hungry. Their breath steams in the cold air. They pace back and forth on the dark earth, waiting.

I've been living with risk and calculation for so long. But I've never been afraid like this. My blood goes so cold that I think my heart will stop. Just moving feels like needles under my skin. But we can't stay here.

'A man can outrun a wolf, you know. It's been said.'

Pasha speaks thoughtfully, scratching his chin as he watches through the window at the shadows passing back and forth, closer and closer to the door.

'Not for too long, not for very far. But a short distance, maybe half a mile, maybe as far as the road. If he ran fast. If he carried nothing. If he didn't fall. If he was lucky.'

He turns to look at me.

'I am a lucky man. It's been said, many times'

In the half-light of the moon through the cracked glass, I see that he is smiling. His teeth are blackened stumps. His face is a ruin of red veins, craggy wrinkles and cracks, and his monstrous nose is a three decade monument to vodka and samogon. But his eyes are shining, and he stands very straight, as if at attention. I see the ghost of a young man with a proud smile, standing with his comrades, receiving high honours.

'Pasha', I say. 'You are a crazy old bastard. You couldn't outrun a lame dog.'

He smiles even wider because I don't get the joke. He picks up his hatchet from the windowsill, hefts it in his gloved hand. The blade glints. The hatchet is sharp.

'Me? Who said anything about me?'

He turns for the door. I grab at his arm, suddenly understanding, and he catches my wrist hard, stronger than I could have imagined. He pulls me close so his terrible face is just inches from mine. His eyes are not shining. They are burning.

'Go out the back door. Run. Run fast. They don't go past the edge of the forest. You should be safe once you see the road, but just in case, keep running. Don't look back. Get to the car. If you can find it. Start running now.'

He drops my wrist and turns away, striding to the door. He is finished with me.

'Pasha', I say, backing away. 'They'll kill you. Don't go out there.'

He throws the door open, and stands for a moment at the threshold of the cottage. Outlined by the moonlight, his shadow is thrown back across the wooden floor. It is impossibly tall and black, and the shadow hatchet in its hand looks as big as a tree. The wolves begin to howl. They are very close. Pasha laughs and howls back, and walks out to meet them.

I turn away, and start to run.

Crutches

Brian Wilson

I have had Jorge Luis Borge's *Ficciones* on loan for seventeen years. I say me, but that's not entirely true. It was my brother who borrowed it. He got it from the Linen Hall Library in 1993. My brother was a terrific reader. Me, personally – I don't do a lot of reading. But it wound up in my possession nevertheless.

Ficciones has been stabilizing a wobbly table in the kitchen for six of those seventeen years. Once, at a car boot sale on the Crumlin Road, my wife saw a blue, chalk paint table. I don't buy anything at car boot sales. Most people there just want to trick you. But there was no convincing my wife. She never noticed the table was wobbly because it was standing in the grass. The woman selling it probably pressed the legs down into the earth.

When we got home my wife was very disappointed. One of the legs was about half an inch shorter than the rest. I don't remember how much she paid for it – twenty quid or something. Still, nobody likes to feel like they've been done over. That's when I remembered the copy of *Ficciones*. It was sitting on top of the empty fish tank in the spare room. I grabbed the book and wiped the dust off the cover with a piece of kitchen roll. Then I placed it under the table's gammy leg. The book fit perfectly.

That night we ate dinner in silence. On the way home from the boot sale I'd given my wife an earful. I told her that she was a fool for buying used up junk. Why not fork out a few extra quid for something decent? Besides, we didn't actually need a new kitchen table. The old one was perfectly fine. Even though I'd fixed the table for her she just sat there staring at her plate.

Now we're getting rid of the table. She wants the room redecorated so that means no more chalk blue. This time everything will be pale violet. I try not to get angry at my wife. In the past I've been told that I have a terrible temper, but I don't think that's true. I get mad when people do stupid things. How can that not be logical?

Last week I came home from work to find the wobbly table was gone. The first thing I did was wonder about *Ficciones*. I spent the next hour and a half looking for it, combing the kitchen and then moving through the rest of the house. Fortunately I had no idea where my wife was. I was furious.

Turns out she was down at B&Q in Holywood looking at green furniture paint. Why she was browsing paint before choosing a table I have no clue. When she returned I really couldn't help myself. I started shouting at her and accusing her of all sorts of things. I know it was cruel, but it was also justified. She had thrown *Ficciones* in the blue recycling bin next to the shed. Just slid it out from under the table and discarded it.

It was raining when I went outside to retrieve it, which is tough on account of my missing foot. I have a pair of crutches I use for getting around, but I was concerned they might slip on the damp concrete. I had no choice but to hop to the bin.

I fished the book out from the bottom of the bin and placed it in a plastic Tesco bag, wrapping it up tight. When I got back inside I removed the book to check there was no water damage.

On the way to the spare room I caught a glimpse of myself in the hall mirror. My hair was damp and my skin was red and blotchy. I didn't want to look at the book any more. I considered placing it back on top of the fish tank, but we'll soon be getting rid of that. *Ficciones* sat there for almost five years before I used it to balance the kitchen table. Hard to believe, but there were actually fish in the tank back then. They were mostly tropical, a few bala sharks and a couple clown loaches. There was even a galaxy rasbora.

The reason the book was there in the first place was to keep the feeding flap down. For some reason it started naturally listing upwards. I thought that might be dangerous for the fish, so I used *Ficciones* to close it. Now all the fish are gone.

Where to put the book, then? I don't know. I still haven't decided. I've been carrying the damn thing around all week. Can't risk putting it down for more than a minute or my wife will probably throw it out again. I just need to find somewhere suitable so that I can forget about it. But the place has to be right.

A couple times I've actually been tempted to read it. I've been bringing it to work every day. I have to get the bus to the office because of my disability, which takes about forty-five minutes give or take. Twice now I've pulled it out of my bag only to do nothing but stare at the cover.

On the front is a picture of an old, white-haired man. I assume this is Borges. He looks to be in his seventies. I've still got a while to go before I reach that age. More than a decade, thank goodness. Part of his face is covered by a large black mark. I have no idea whether Borges is still alive or not, but he's got one of those names that makes me think probably not. It's the kind of name you'd gloss over in a book store; an old story written by someone long dead.

Ficciones. God, isn't that a boring title for a book? I've never heard of Jorge Luis Borges but that's not the sort of name that inspires me to try more reading. On the contrary, it's exactly the kind of thing my brother liked. Long, foreign names. Novels that sound like you need a university degree to even turn to the first page. Christ.

Before it sat on the fish tank, *Ficciones* was in a shoe box under my wife and I's double bed. It sat there untouched for a very long time. I kept meaning to return it to the library, but I never got round to it. Would you believe I actually bought a pair of shoes just so I'd have a box to put it in? I know that sounds ludicrous, and it is. I don't know what the hell I was thinking. It's embarrassing to remember now.

I wonder if it mightn't be a good idea to put it under the bed again. These days I sleep in the spare room with the empty fish tank. The room is small but there's enough space for a bed and a chest of drawers. Besides, in here I wouldn't have to worry about my wife stealing it. Come to think of it, though, I've got nothing to put it in. It can't very well just lie there on the floor.

I had always assumed *Ficciones* was a novel, but it appears to be a collection of short stories. I know this because last night I opened it for the first time. Yes, the first time in seventeen years. Maybe that seems odd, but what reason did I have to open it before? I had no interest in reading it. Now that there's a chance my wife might throw it out, I figured I should take a look inside. As I thought, Jorge Luis Borges is dead. He died in 1986.

I also found the Linen Hall Library ticket glued to the interior of the front cover. My brother's name was the last to be stamped, his signature scrawled next to the stamp's blue ink. It's hard to believe that the Linen Hall Library is still standing. So much about Belfast has changed in the last three decades. It's tough having lived through violence. You'd wonder how something like a library could remain. I don't know the exact date, but I remember my brother telling me that the library first opened over two-hundred years ago. That's impressive, even for someone who doesn't read books.

Despite having stood for over two-hundred years, I've only been in the Linen Hall Library once, on the day I crossed paths with *Ficciones*. I was there with my brother. I'd lent him some money the month before and we'd met to discuss repayment. I don't mean to be crass, but my brother didn't have much money. If they paid people to read books he'd have had no problem at all, but that's not the way the world works.

Instead, he was employed part-time at the Ulster Museum. Who knows what the hell he did during the rest of the week. I never met any of his girlfriends.

We went for coffee somewhere in the centre of Belfast, in a little café that went under years ago. The money was so he could pay rent on his flat for the next three months. His landlord was threatening to evict him due to multiple failed payments. I'll admit that I was reluctant to help, but I decided since I'm older that it was my duty to bail him out this once. Still, I had no intention of being robbed, so we met to arrange a strict repayment schedule.

After coffee we still had some stipulations to lay down. He suggested we take a walk while ironing everything out. Payment was due on the twenty-eighth of each month before nine p.m, and was to be no less than agreed. If he wanted to pay more and square things off sooner, that was okay by me.

Before I knew it we'd arrived at the Linen Hall Library, where my brother told me he'd like to look around for ten minutes. I said that was fine. I have no doubt when he picked out *Ficciones* that he told me all about Borges. He was always trying to explain to me about writers, suggesting different stories and poems. I think he knew this made me feel uncomfortable. I could never understand that sort of thing the way he did. On that particular day I wasn't in the mood to hear about another pretentious artist. I was irritated – irritated that he'd got himself into another financial mess, irritated that I'd cracked and decided to help him. But mostly I was irritated by the fact that even in the midst of our talk he had to go and get himself another damned book.

After we left the library we walked back to city hall. My brother was running late for his shift at the museum so he wanted to get the bus. This annoyed me even more. How long would he have a job if he kept up like this? He didn't even tell me he was working until after we'd left the building.

Another bus was due in five minutes. He sat down on the seat at the stop while I remained standing. I told him that he needed to straighten his life out. I don't think he was listening. When the bus arrived he shook my hand and said he'd see me on the twenty-eighth of next month. I squeezed his fingers and turned to walk away.

As I did I noticed that he'd left *Ficciones* on the seat next to the stop. The bus hadn't moved yet. I picked up the book and turned to see him sitting by the window. He was looking straight ahead. Before I could react there was a flash of light and then the whole of Belfast fell silent. The next part is fragmented. I remember heat. I also remember blood. Then everything was swallowed up by a thick, black cloud.

No group ever claimed responsibility for the attack. I have my beliefs, other people have theirs. I try not to get sucked into all that any more. Like I said, Belfast has changed a lot in the last three decades. This place is always changing. My brother died instantly along with four other people. Among the dozen injured was myself with my lost foot.

Somehow the book travelled with me to the hospital. Maybe I was still clutching it when I was picked up by the ambulance. Regardless, that's how *Ficciones* fell into my possession. When I was finally discharged I placed it on the drawer next to my wife and I's bed. She didn't like that. It made her incredibly upset. Surprisingly, the book remained in remarkable condition. The cover was a bit blackened and there was some singeing around the edges, but that's about it. Even so, seeing it there, my wife would always cry. She cried so much and so often that I went out and bought a pair of shoes. Of course, I only needed one. I mainly wanted the box. That made her cry even more. So now I'm left with the question: where next after the wobbly kitchen table?

I can hear my wife shuffling around in the kitchen. She always drinks a glass of water before bed. That's something I don't understand. Every night without fail she gets up in the middle of the night to use the bathroom. It used to drive me crazy, because it always woke me up, too.

Why drink the water if she knows it's only going to make her need to pee?

Lately I haven't been sleeping. I get into bed and then I start to sweat. There is no more drifting off. It's a struggle to get over for even a couple hours. I know that I won't sleep until I do something with *Ficciones*. Lying in bed, I can't stop thinking about the picture of Borges on the front cover: the deep, black scar that obscures part of his face. Tomorrow I will return the book to the Linen Hall Library. There is no reason for me to hold on to it. Seventeen years is quite enough. Then again, maybe I can find a use for it.

Silence from the kitchen. My wife must be finished poking around. We haven't talked about our sleeping arrangement in several months. At this point it has just become normal.

I sit up and throw my legs off the bed. My crutches are propped against the fish tank. I reach over and slide my arms into them before attempting to stand up. It's quite easy now, but occasionally I will still lose my balance. I haven't fallen in around two years, but it's always a possibility. A couple years after I lost my foot I took a fall on the way out of work. Went straight down and fractured my jaw. Now I try to be careful.

I cross the hall into the kitchen, *Ficciones* tucked under my arm. It's dark, but I decide not to turn on the light.

There's a white cardboard box leaning against the fridge. Inside is the new kitchen table. It's made from faded oak and has already been painted green. Since I can't sleep maybe it would be a good idea to build the table. My wife has been pestering me about it for the past three days. We've been eating our dinner on trays in front of the television. She hates doing that.

I ease the box flat onto the linoleum floor, then I head out to the shed in the back garden. I return with a Stanley knife, a torch, a ruler, a saw and a few extra tools. They're in a plastic bag hanging from one of my crutches.

When the box has been sliced open I set to work constructing the table, using the torch on the floor for guidance. Even though my wife's bedroom is upstairs I make sure to be as quiet as possible. After I saw the wood I stop for a minute to listen for any signs of stirring.

I really wish my wife would let me do the furniture shopping. Somehow she always manages to buy stuff that's damaged or broken. That's one thing that really ticks me off. God knows things haven't been great between us recently, but when I try to do something nice I'm made to feel like an idiot.

Using my crutches I stand up and examine the completed table. Christ, does the woman buy whatever worthless junk is set in front of her? Once again she's managed to buy a gimped, rickety table.

Ficciones. Returning to my knees I place the book beneath the maimed leg. Then I test the stability. It's perfect.

While clearing up the tools I curse my wife's stupidity. Well, she's got no-one to blame but herself. One of these days I'm going to return *Ficciones* to the library. What's she going to do then? I'm not paying for another table.

Back in the spare room I place my crutches against the fish tank and climb into bed. As I lie down something sharp digs into my side. I remove the piece of wood from my pocket and drop it through the fish tank's broken feeding flap.

My old bedroom is directly above me. I stare at the ceiling for ten or fifteen minutes. I see Borges again with his scorched and wrinkled face. Then I begin to cry.

Parrot Tulips

Eleanor Ford

Red and gold in the borders at home
I mark their arrival late each spring,
how, shaking their feathered heads awake
they come as carnival queens with their petals
rinsed, polished and curled.

They rise between forget-me-nots,
flamenco dresses hung out to dry
upside down on invisible washing lines.
They are the members of an extravagant tea service,
teacups set out on a fan of chartreuse.

They are *Tulipa* 'Flaming Parrot'
in primrose-yellow, defined by another bloom
as if always dressing in the colours of another,
primrose-yellow with yellow-green streaks,
crimson shot through a ruffle of silk.

Forest of Beech Trees

Eleanor Ford

I could stand for a long time
in front of Klimt's
Forest of Beech Trees

and find a dozen ways
through or none at all.
The beech leaves have fallen,

there is a horizon –
I can see it between trees
but I have not reached it.

Even now I am not certain
if I will live in the hills
or on the plainlands.

Those beech trees of Klimt's,
their flaking red leaves
are a bed of hot coals.

The Architect's Men

Eleanor Ford

Planting their timbers into the sleech
they added their part to that forest beneath the city
and formed a ribcage of stakes, some as long as fifty feet,
four double colonnades to keep their cathedral afloat.

Only after this did they raise their pillars of stone,
setting each pillar over a timber brother below
so that one length mirrored the other,
in secret symmetry, on either side of the marbled floor.

Heatwave

Eleanor Ford

August. Caravans and tents
in a field, on a dairy farm
two miles inland, sit under
the shadow of Penberry Rock

A very hot summer that year, that second week of August and how
well they remembered the stifling borrowed caravan. They'd
rather have slept outside, or in one of the little tents that shimmered in
a brilliant nylon border around the field. They envied the cows, so still,
except for a trudge to the dairy each morning and evening, spending
life out on the farm, cutting grass. They couldn't bear to travel more
than two miles, the car was so hot, the seatbelt buckles burning. At
least inland there was some shade. They told their children to keep
under the awning and stave off heatstroke. They learnt the shadows of
their neighbours before they learnt their faces. Penberry grew huge and
oppressive. They turned their backs on the rock.

From the Roadside

Eleanor Ford

Driving out to Aberdovey
we stop for petrol in a small village.

There are grey terraced houses,
grey faces at windows

and there is a church
and a churchyard and a child

carrying her wreath to a graveside;
a girl, maybe five or six,

her hair in curls
and a man, – her father? –

stamping down his cigarette
as he leans heavy on the lychgate.

When the tank is full we drive on
but we cannot forget her.

She seemed so small, to be holding
all that weight in her hands.

The Night Rises Up

Tara West

Andrew never runs like this, not for peelers, not for anybody. It surprises him, the way you might marvel at your speed if you leapt off a building. Adrenaline gives Andrew wings. He is unstoppable, unbeatable, the fastest man in the estate tonight, but if he wants to run faster he will have to drop the TV. Because the man who owns it is not giving up.

The slapping sound of their shoes bounces off the parked cars in the dark street. In one backward glance, Andrew sees the man's shorts, T-shirt, trainers and shaved head as he passes under a streetlight. The man charges through Andrew's trail of haphazard breaths, his own breathing short and controlled. Trust Andrew to rob the house of the fittest man in the estate. There are maybe thirty paces between them.

Andrew needs this TV. He has a buyer. The buyer is his mother. She wants a 19' widescreen wall-mountable Samsung for the kitchen and by fuck, it's heavy. She could've warned him. The corner is already damaged where he dropped it getting it off the wall. She wouldn't notice. It's a nice TV, but the man wants it back. The man doesn't shout or scream, the way most of them do. Most people are muppets. This man just runs.

Andrew can hear his own breath, scraping and desperate like a dog on a lead. Behind him, the man's breathing is hard and even, making Andrew think of machinery. Jesus shit, he's fast. Andrew lets the TV fall to the ground and bits of it shatter and crush. He twists between two parked cars, across the road and down a shadowy alley. Keep your TV, you fucken mentaller.

But the man still follows, a juggernaut of flesh, because the TV is not enough. Shit shit shit. Andrew is used to running these streets, it's where he grew up, where he lit bins and farts, drank Buckie and Olde English, got off his nuts on whizz or blow and tried a swig of paraffin for a laugh. Bad idea. This is another one. What the hell? What the frig? This man isn't normal.

Andrew remembers the remote control is still jammed in his pocket. He wriggles it out and lobs it at the man. It crashes and splits on a wall, but the man doesn't stop. At the end of the alley, Andrew takes a sharp left towards the Chinese takeaway, his feet sliding on dog crap, his arms spiraling. He squawks, regains his balance and runs on.

Mr Lin turns the key in the lock of the graffitied shutter, closing the takeaway for the night. He watches the pair sprint by. The younger one came in drunk last week; he dropped his curry chips outside and launched 150 menus into the street like pink birds. Mr Lin hopes the running man catches him. A swell of adrenaline shuttles Mr Lin to his old Nissan and he drives away quickly, hoping not to see them again.

Andrew's steps lose rhythm as he runs. His feet splay to the side and his heart and lungs shudder like jelly. He has a stitch, like this is school or something. Why doesn't the man just fuck off? He has his TV. Andrew grabs a hedge and uses it to take a corner at speed. He can't go back to his ma's, he can't go to Lauren's, the man might follow. Past the bus shelter, where he notices new glass. Takes a lot more effort to smash one of those than you might think.

Andrew is slowing, he can't help it, his legs are too heavy. His jelly heart is pulsing up his throat and he thinks he might spew it up. He is the fastest man only for the time it takes to run away, but he has never had to run this far. If he doesn't slow down he will stumble, and if he falls, the man will use his feet on him. It shouldn't happen, it never happens, people don't keep chasing like this, but it is happening, and this man is going to kick him to death over a stupid fucken TV. This is his ma's fault. What was wrong with the colour portable he got her four fucken years ago?

Andrew is all elbows, ankles, knees and chin. Every limb is attached to a string he can't see and every breath causes him pain. The blank houses, parked cars, pavement, hedges - everything jolts and jumps as he tries to keep going. He can smell the trees of the park ahead. Beyond the park, the factory. Behind him, the man.

They cross the pensioners' gardens. Each pensioner lies in bed dreaming of Andrew getting his shit kicked in, Andrew knows it. He remembers stealing their Christmas decorations, damaging their cars, getting a guilty kick when he made them cower and moan. One of the old ladies watches him through her yellow net curtains and clucks her false teeth. He needs a good slap, he does, God help him.

Andrew breaks through the bushes into the park, hearing small things scatter at his feet. His ankles twist on trash and his clothes catch on thorns, like the bushes want to hold onto him - this mean little shit who set fire to them and polluted them with his cans and condoms. Andrew's fingers work at the thorns and he yanks himself free, hands slick with blood. The bushes slice at his calves for good measure.

He plunges into darkness, every breath amplified in the open. Ahead, the factory's security light makes paths across the grass. Andrew crouches by the trees, panting, trembling, throat clicking. He knows the park, it's where he was spawned, where he played football, where he bunked off, where he became a father himself. He hears fissling and crunching from the bushes behind him. Jesus, the man has super powers, he has night vision, what the fuck?

Andrew limps on, surprising himself with a moan. He claws across the ditch between the park and the factory. The thick mud pulls and sucks at his feet till it steals one of his shoes. He goes on without it, ducking through the hole in the fence, and even the fence wants a piece of him, snagging his jacket and ripping his sleeve. Behind him, the runner's even breathing comes through the dark, his trainers thudding on the grass. The man is a nutjob. He wants to kill Andrew.

'It was only a fucken TV, mate!' Andrew yelps as he scurries into the factory grounds, past the main factory building, round the side and into shadow.

There is no reply.

Andrew slips between two warehouses, wincing as his shoeless foot finds every twig and stone. They always find bodies with one shoe on. That will be him in the morning. He struggles to listen, but his heartbeat gets in the way.

What did the man want? He'd left his own windows and door open in the middle of the night, what did he expect? It wasn't Andrew's fault. Although it was Andrew's fault for not realising the man might actually still be in the house. Twat.

At the end of the building, Andrew can see the factory gate and beyond it, the road. He strains to hear above his own noisy breathing, but the only sound is the occasional car passing beyond the gate. The man's gone. He's lost him. Andrew is grateful to he doesn't know what. He grips his knees, shaking his head like a footballer who's missed a goal. Maybe he'll give up house breaking for a while.

He can't go back to his ma's without a fucken 19' widescreen wall-mountable Samsung. He limps to the gate and hauls himself over it, swearing as it rattles and clangs. He lands awkwardly on heavy legs and a hand extends through the gate and yanks him back. He can feel the wet heat of the runner's breath, see his small teeth and smell his grassy sweat as the man pulls him close and punches at his scrawny head. Andrew twists and squirms and flails out onto the road.

Mr Lin's Nissan is the fastest car in the estate tonight. It's doing 38mph and it misses Andrew and hits the runner. The fittest man in the estate, the man who can run marathons, vault obstacles and chase skinny little shitheads, but not actually catch them. Mr Lin's car lifts the runner off his feet and he thuds up over the windscreen and down the driver side.

Mr Lin brakes, not knowing who or what he's hit. The runner lies on the road beside the car and Andrew backs away, watching Mr Lin unmoving in his seat. That looks messy. It wasn't Andrew's fault. Dickhead didn't know how to cross the fucken road, did he? Andrew turns and takes the nearest alley. Saunter. Just saunter. There'll be another TV.

Slowly, the runner pushes himself to his feet.

Second Chance Academy

Noel Russell

FADE IN.

INT. BEDROOM. BEFORE DAWN - CONTINUOUS

OSCAR MORGAN, a man in his 50s, sits bolt upright in bed in his pyjamas.

He looks at his wife, reaches for a notebook and pen on the bedside table, can't get it, so lifts an I-Phone and dictates.

> OSCAR
> Her rich brown hair curls down
> onto her shoulders, the straps of
> her ivory nightdress bright on her
> olive skin - female, beautiful,
> other. Men sailed to Troy for
> this.

Then - it could be an earthquake. Or a bin lorry passing.
The windows rattle. A glass of water trembles on his
bedside table.

BERNADETTE, in her 50s, sucks in air, gives a long shameless walrus
blow-out of snores through mouth and nose.

> OSCAR
> A sudden burst of angry snorts.
> Furious, brazen, filthy, a Banzai
> wave of depravity. No man can live
> with this. No man should have to.

He nudges her with his knee, but it's no use.

> OSCAR
> Greedy, shocking, squalid.

He cringes under the bedclothes, then sticks his head out just as another volley, half human, half animal, hits him.

> OSCAR
> Jesus Mary and St Joseph! Incline
> unto my aid O God. O Lord make
> haste to help me!

He slides out of bed as if under gunfire, but knocks over the unsteady stacks of books on the floor and table. From the bed a voice speaks.

> BERNADETTE
> (sleepily)
> Do you want a bloody hammer?

He closes his eyes and breathes out - the start of a new day for Oscar Morgan.

INT. KITCHEN - LATER

Oscar is alone in the shabby kitchen. He is wearing a Family Guy Peter Griffin Merry Christmas Everybody! apron.

OSCAR
Mr Pussy! Mr Pussy! Mr Pusseee!

The cat appears and rubs himself against Oscar's leg.
Oscar lifts him onto his shoulder, pets and feeds him.

OSCAR
Who's a good boy?

Oscar fills the kettle and makes porridge.

Bernadette walks in, still with the looks that turned his head 30 years
ago, but with a woman-in-her-50s' figure.

OSCAR
Sleep well?

BERNADETTE
Till some weirdo started wrecking
the place.

Oscar retrieves his porridge, pulls off a near black banana from a bunch
and slices it in.

Bernadette puts the last slice of bread, a heel, into the toaster.

OSCAR
I'm not sleeping well.

BERNADETTE
You've a really weird snore, know that?
Sounds like you're having a stroke.

> OSCAR
> Really? I never heard it.

> BERNADETTE
> You don't. You're fast asleep.

RORY,(17), sullen, comes in, fills a pint glass full of orange juice and leaves the empty carton in the fridge.

> OSCAR
> Hi Rory. Don't worry about
> anybody else.

Rory covers his ears with his giant headphones.

> OSCAR
> Maybe some day, when I'm not here,
> you'll realise your da was right
> about something.

KATE,(16), sleepy and sullen, comes in and takes out a cereal box. It's empty.

> KATE
> I hate this house!

> OSCAR
> Have a banana. They're good
> for you.

> KATE
> They're disgusting. Look at them.
> They're too old.

>   OSCAR
>   That's just the skin. They're still
>   good inside.

>   KATE
>   *Like don't judge a book by its*
>   *cover?* Wrong. If it's past its
>   sell-by date, it's past it
>   forever, Banana Man.

She finds the empty carton in the fridge.

>   KATE
>   Why are we always short of stuff?

>   OSCAR
>   That stuff's bad for your teeth.
>   Strips the enamel, exposes the
>   nerves.

>   KATE
>   Mine are still ok thanks. Take a
>   look at your own.

Oscar's I-phone goes off and Kate presses the dictation button by mistake. Bernadette's snoring comes out, loud and proud, bouncing off the kitchen walls.

>   OSCAR
>   Give me that.

Oscar tries to get it but Kate runs with it and loudens it.

> BERNADETTE
> You getting crank calls or
> something?

> OSCAR
> These downloads, I can never
> get the hang of them.

He moves towards Kate, but:

> OSCAR V/O
> A sudden burst of angry snorts.
> Furious, brazen, filthy, a Banzai
> wave of depravity.

Oscar catches Kate but she throws it to Rory who plays the snoring at full volume. Oscar grabs it just as it plays:

> OSCAR V.O.
> Jesus Mary and St Joseph!

He turns it off. She waits for his answer.

> OSCAR
> It was just an exercise. You
> know – getting the creative juices
> flowing.

> BERNADETTE
> I know what I'd like to get
> flowing.

Oscar squirms.

EXT. SCHOOL – DAY

Oscar rides his bike through a flood of boys going into a soulless modern school.

He takes his briefcase, locks the bike up, and is swept along in the tide of teenage energy.

INT. CLASSROOM - DAY

Oscar is at the front of a class of 16 year old boys, noisy, pushing, ignoring him.

> OSCAR
> Sit down. Now!

Sullenly they sit down.

> OSCAR
> Open your books. Page 128.
> Tucker you read.

> TUCKER
> I can't read sir.

> OSCAR
> That's not entirely true Tucker.

> TUCKER
> I forgot my glasses actually.

> OSCAR
> I've never seen you with glasses.

> TUCKER
> I use them when I have no lenses
> left.

The thickos make 'Goggles' signs and shout 'Hi Specy!' at him.

> OSCAR
> That's enough. I'll read.
> He does as Tucker starts texting
> on his phone.

> OSCAR
> I sought a theme and sought for it
> in vain,/I sought it daily for six
> weeks or so/Maybe at last, being
> but a broken man/

One of the boys pretends to yawn, his mates laugh. Oscar catches them
on.

> OSCAR
> You'd better be paying attention.
> I'll be asking questions.
> Tucker makes a hidden wanker sign.

> OSCAR
> .../Winter and summer till old age
> began/My circus animals were all
> on show,/ Those stilted boys, that
> burnished chariot,/ Lion and woman
> and the Lord knows what.'

OSCAR

So what's Yeats talking about
here?

BOY#1

Something about a circus sir.
A lion and a woman. Is he a lion
tamer or something?

OSCAR

No. He's not a lion tamer. He's a
poet. That's just a metaphor.

BOY#2

So why does he say he's got a
circus when he hasn't got one?
Lions and all.

OSCAR

It's a figure of speech. Like
'he's a lion in battle.' He uses
a word or a phrase to suggest a
resemblance to something else.

BOY#3

So he has no lions then? Wanker.

OSCAR

Language Flynn.

Flynn shakes his head in disgust.

> OSCAR
>
> Let's hear a bit more. Any
> volunteers?

No chance.

> OSCAR
>
> Great.

He quickly gets into it, oblivious to their discomfort.

> OSCAR
>
> What can I but enumerate old
> themes?/First that sea-rider Oisin
> led by the nose/through three
> enchanted islands...

He senses their restlessness and boredom.

> OSCAR
>
> Who's Oisin?

Nobody knows.

> FLYNN
>
> I know sir. He rides horses. In the
> circus.

Guffaws all round.

OSCAR

Oisin is a mythical figure, who lives in the Land of Eternal Youth...so Yeats is talking about beauty and age. And something else? Anybody? No?

Not likely.

OSCAR

He's asking himself the value of his work...a question we all of course must ask ourselves at some time.

BOY#2

Did he make good money Sir? Was he rich?

OSCAR

Not rich but not poor. He did ok.

BOY#3

So what's he gurnin' about sir? Twat.

Cheers.

OSCAR

Settle down. Here's the climax: Now that my ladder's gone,/I must lie down where all the ladders start,/In the foul rag-and-boneshop of the heart./

                    BOY#1
        What's he doin' lying down in a
        gypo's shop?

                    OSCAR
        That's another metaphor.
        Understand? He must... write out
        of his personal turmoil, the foul
        rag and bone shop of the heart.
        That's what he's saying. And
        that's what so brave about it.

Flynn puts his hand up.

                    FLYNN
        Who nicked his ladder sir?
        Tosser!
        Cheers, claps, whistles, foot
        stamping.

                    OSCAR
        Enough! That's enough I said.
        Shut up you moron! Shut up!
        The whole fuckin' lot of you!

The class is stunned into silence.

EXT. CYCLE PATH - SATURDAY MORNING.

Oscar and two mates ride along the cycle path on the shores of Belfast
Lough, in stretched lycra.

ARTHUR, is bespectacled, losing his hair and carrying weight, while JOHNNY, is slimmer and taller.

Oscar has the best bike but Johnny on a hybrid soon races ahead.

Oscar gives chase and before long the pair race each other, scattering dog walkers, old couples and missing children by inches.

Furious parents scream abuse at them and one irate father chases them on his bike. But the two lunatics leave him behind in their frantic race, while Arthur catches the flak.

Oscar pulls away and lands first into a McDonald's.

Johnny, sweat-drenched and breathing heavily, arrives followed by a red-faced Arthur.

> OSCAR
>> The usual?

He orders and smiles at some young women cyclists who are in the queue in front of him. They give him a brush-off smile.

Oscar comes down to the mates' table with coffee and muffins.

> JOHNNY
>> I've no change. Square you up
>> later, ok?

> ARTHUR
>> No problem.

Arthur counts out his change and gives it to Oscar.

OSCAR
What was all that about?

JOHNNY
I was only trying to create a safe
distance and you came racing
past like Lance Armstrong.

OSCAR
Safe distance? I was just trying
to get past you to avoid the
embarrassment.

JOHNNY
So that's why you nearly killed
those kids? To avoid the
embarrassment.

OSCAR
If you got a half decent bike we
could all stay together.
Maybe you can get me one when
you finish your novel. Or was it
start it? Or win Who Wants To Be
a Millionaire?

A family with three children on small bikes that they
passed come in and the parents give them dirty looks.
Oscar and Johnny keep their heads down.

ARTHUR

Talking of money, guess who I
heard from?

JOHNNY

Beyonce?

JIM

Paddy Moran.

OSCAR

Don't tell me. He wants to start
fracking under Tara.

JOHNNY

Very bright guy. Done brilliantly
for himself.

OSCAR

That's what worries me about this
country.

JOHNNY

You're just jealous of him. The
guy's a genius.

OSCAR

He's a greedy, philistine chancer.
The type of guy who's brought
the Republic to its knees.

ARTHUR

He's invited our year down to
his new hotel in the West. All
expenses paid.

OSCAR

Sounds awful.

JOHNNY

All the oul' crowd'll be there.
The Blue Bus Kid, Shake
McGahey, Mickey McGlone.
And it will get us away from the
spouses for a weekend. What's
not to like?

OSCAR

All those tired old men in one
room, all there for a lick of
Paddy Moran's lolly. Ugh!

JOHNNY

Speak for yourself. Those places
are crawling with snatch at the
weekend. Weddings, hen parties.
It's skank city. Even you might
get lucky.

OSCAR

Thanks. I try not to flirt with
women who are younger than my
daughter.

Johnny looks round McDonalds.

JOHNNY

That must be why you weren't
chatting up those hotties at the
counter.

OSCAR

Just talking about bikes. They've
all got Colnagos. Latest models.

JOHNNY

Latest models. Right. Come on.
Let's go to this Paddy thing. You
might pick up a few tips on how
to make your fortune.

OSCAR

And you're gonna knock them
out with one of your bright ideas.
Or is it the hit album this week?

ARTHUR

Gentlemen. Please. We can loathe
those who have done better than
us, pity those who have done
worse, and share special bonding
moments with the other
mediocrities like ourselves. And
the drink is free. In strictly cost
benefit terms, it is a no brainer.

OSCAR

You goin'?

                    ARTHUR
          We are considering our options.
          And looking favourably on it,
          schedules permitting.

                    OSCAR
          Count me out.

                    JOHNNY
          Who dares wins, eh?

INT. RESTAURANT. DAY – BELFAST

It's Mother's day in a down market Italian restaurant.
The place is full of families treating elderly women and son-in-laws
doing their best to be civil.
The Morgans are there with Bernadette's mother LIZZIE, 70s, sharp.

Oscar scans the menu anxiously.

                    OSCAR
          The pizzas are really good here.

                    RORY
          I want the swordfish.

                    KATE
          I want the fillet steak.

The waitress comes and everybody orders the expensive choices. Oscar
frets.

                    OSCAR
          Pizza for me. You have small
          sizes?

WAITRESS

We do children's.

Rory and Kate smirk.

OSCAR

The adult will do fine.

KATE

And a large glass of Chianti for
me. Mum?

LIZZIE

A wee vodka and lemonade for me.

OSCAR

And bring some water. From the
tap.

WAITRESS

We only serve bottled water sir.

OSCAR

Ok. Bottled water.

The waitress goes.

LIZZIE

You'll never guess who I was
speaking to.

BERNADETTE

Who?

> LIZZIE
> Betty Moran. She says her Paddy
> is doing brilliant.

Oscar rolls his eyes.

> BERNADETTE
> He's on the Sunday Times rich
> list.

Oscar sips on his water, fuming.

The waitress brings his rather small pizza. Rory and Kate burst out laughing.

INT. RESTAURANT - LATER

The waitress brings the bill to Oscar. He tries to pay with a credit card. It doesn't go through. He offers another and that is refused too.

> OSCAR
> You sure the machine's working ok?

> WAITRESS
> It has worked for everybody else
> sir.

Flustered and embarrassed, Oscar opens his wallet. He searches for notes and pulls out a single fiver.

The whole table's watching him.

> OSCAR
>
> Could've sworn I had twenties.
> Must have slipped out of my
> pocket.

Bernadette reaches for one of her credit cards as Oscar keeps searching for the 'lost' notes.

INT. PRINCIPAL'S OFFICE. DAY

The principal RUTH TURNER is in her early 40s, slim, wearing fashionable spectacles and expensive clothes.

Oscar walks in and stands like a pupil at her desk. She finally turns to him.

> RUTH TURNER
>
> Have a seat Mr Morgan.

Oscar sits down, exasperated, knocking his knee against her desk.

> RUTH TURNER
>
> I have had a letter from Bernard
> Flynn's mother.

> OSCAR
>
> I'm surprised.

> RUTH TURNER
>
> Why?

> OSCAR
>
> She can actually write? That's
> obviously where her son gets his
> literary skills from.

                    RUTH TURNER
          I'll read it, shall I?

                       OSCAR
          Be my guest.

She reads like a judge from the letter.

                    RUTH TURNER
          '...and then Mr Morgan turned
          round and started swearing like
          a...(pause as she edits out the
          f... word)trooper and my Bernard
          was traumatised and he hasn't
          been at himself since. It's a ...
          (Pause as she edits another
          f...) disgrace so it is using
          language like that to young boys.
          He needs sorted out. Yours
          sincerely Mrs Colette Flynn. PS
          My Tommy's (pause as she edits
          again)... ragin'. He'll fix him
          for you in two seconds.'

                       OSCAR
          Her little angel Bernard was
          totally out of line.

                    RUTH TURNER
          Mmm. You weren't totally out of
          control?

OSCAR

Listen. You have to draw the line
with them. Believe me, I've been
teaching them for 30 years.

RUTH TURNER

Maybe you should try a new
approach. There's a full range of
very exciting courses available.
Making literature innovative and
compelling for young people.

OSCAR

Most of them can hardly write
their names. They are going to
have compelling careers in a full
range of young offenders centres.

RUTH TURNER

Patricia Mullan couldn't speak
more highly of her course.

OSCAR

That says it all.

RUTH TURNER

Patricia has been working very
closely with me on the new
curriculum material.
She's doing a great job. Full of
new ideas, going forward.

OSCAR

I bet she is. Number one: how to
stay out of the classroom.

RUTH TURNER

They do anger management
courses too.

OSCAR

I do not need a fuckin' anger
management course.

RUTH TURNER

I think maybe you need a little
break. Things seem to be getting
on top of you.

OSCAR

I don't need any little break,
thank you very much.

RUTH TURNER

I think you do. That sort of
behaviour in the class is just not
acceptable. To me or the board of
management.

OSCAR

Listen, Nurse Ratchet, the board
of management know as much
about teaching as my arse knows
about snipe shooting.

> RUTH TURNER
> You'll come back refreshed. Trust
> me.
>> OSCAR
> Trust you? Leave that one with
> me.

> RUTH TURNER
> I think we need some clarity
> here. You're taking some time
> off. From tomorrow. Patricia,
> who is now on my senior
> management team, will arrange
> cover. Enjoy your break.

He watches her, stunned and outgunned, then leaves.

A Day Out

Joanne Higgins

Annemarie felt the car slowing to a stop, outside the hospital gates. Beside her Fat Face stayed quiet, so that the ceaseless ticking over of the engine became a kind of peace.

Her mother took her time getting out of the car, telling him to cut the turnip up before she came home.

'One of the old ones your mother sent.'

'Heh?'

Annemarie watched her father turn down the radio, while he flicked ash with his free hand out the window, juggling between the wheel and the cigarette.

Her mother tried again, this time framing the instruction as a question.

'Damien if you get a minute, would ya chop one of those turnips? Your mother goes to a lot of bother to get them and I don't want to let – I've had to bin a few already.'

Annemarie, and her mother and her sister waited for him to answer. Her father liked them to wait.

Eventually he spoke, 'Aiye. Grand.'

Annemarie knew that her mother ought to be inside at her locker by now.

'I'll be finished at five, okay?' she said getting out.

Annemarie and Fat Face sat like two stones.

Her mother leaned over the passenger seat, 'You'll be alright till then.'

Annemarie goggled her black eyes up to meet her mother's dark look.

'—You'd better get a move on,' her father said readjusting his mirror.

Was it permission she wanted or a guarantee that it would be alright? Annemarie watched her mother holding tightly onto the door, as if that would make any difference to anyone. Her mother tried to sling the navy bag across her shoulder, but it slipped. The shoulder had become sloped in recent years and the strap slid down every time.

Annemarie willed her to let go of the door.

'Annemarie, don't fight with your sister . . . look it's only for the one day.'

It was probably the best her mother could do, before they were gone pulling away, out into the busy road across the white line and back. Annemarie looked behind and saw her watching; the worry and the wonder – *had he taken a drink already?*

But the form was good with him, *hadn't they all seen it?*

Annemarie had poked Fat Face awake that morning and when they'd padded downstairs in their slippers he had stopped swabbing the fireplace with a scouring pad and asked if they wanted *Frosties* or *Coco Pops.*

Annemarie instantly understood – today he had a purpose. She'd overheard the late phone-call that came for her mother, the soft voice agreeing to come into recovery on her day off. Who would look after them, *her father?*

She'd lain awake afterwards, knowing there was nobody else. Maybe – just maybe – they would get through the day and none of them would be dead at the end of it.

*   *   *

On the way to Granny's Annemarie listened to the old stories, again, of his days trudging to school with only a stub of a pencil and a half penny copy book in hand. The mirror was re-positioned with Fat Face's chubby cheeks filling the reflection. Annemarie felt fairly certain he couldn't see her.

'And we had no shoes, bare feet, in the rain!'

'Even in the snow Daddy?'

Annemarie rolled her eyes at Fat Face's pathetic question.

'Frost, snow, ice – all weathers.'

Annemarie was staring out the window at the miserable houses and cars, that made up the town. She muttered under her breath.

'What's your sister sayin'?'

Fat Face peeped over at Annemarie, before meeting her father's eye.

'She says you probably ate dry bread and drank black tea for lunch.'

Annemarie nipped a portion of Fat Face's thigh between her fingers and squeezed hard.

Fat face coloured.

'Cry baby,' mouthed Annemarie screening the motion with her hand.

'— Annemarie's right. We used to walk in the rain, with no shoes, up the hill to get a bit O' dry bread and a cup a cocoa, if you were lucky.'

Annemarie was never 'right'. The humour was definitely good with him.

Granny's house was a tiny bungalow. Annemarie didn't know why it was only ever referred to as 'Granny's House' when Granda lived there too. She seldom saw them. Her father preferred to visit his parents, alone, on Sunday mornings when she was at mass with her mother and Fat Face.

Through the orange-painted gate, Annemarie and Fat Face followed their father around the path of broken concrete.

It felt wrong to Annemarie, going to the back door. They had to pass the rear bedroom. Through the net curtain she picked out a couple of pairs of grey men's trousers stretched across the back of a chair and a bed – smaller than the queen-size her mother and Fat Face shared at home. The bed was definitely a double, meant for two, but only slept in by one judging from the way the clothes had been folded back on one side only.

The Super-ser fire was tight up against the far wall and an ashtray, overflowing with butts, sat under the bed on the slept in side, almost, as if someone had stashed it there in a hurry.

Granny took a long time to come to the door.

Annemarie's father jerked the handle. He gestured to Fat Face to take a step back then put his shoulder to it. Granny, on the other side, pulled inwards. He landed at her feet.

'Damien! What the fuck are ya at?' she said.

At 4 feet 11 inches in height, she hadn't seen the children behind him.

And then when she did, 'Yir mother workin' today?' cool as you like.

In the kitchen Annemarie was a pixie next to Fat Face; her little sister's proportions emphasized by the tight galley. Granny appraised them both out of one dark crack in the interminably folded paper of her face. Annemarie felt the heat of Fat Face's edge closer.

Granny led them in to the living room. Settling back in to the low chair by the fire she withdrew a cigarette pack from the pocket of her apron. Leaning towards the fire for a light, she grimaced and was forced to recoil, unlit, back in to her seat.

'Have you no sense? Would ya let me do it for ya. You're gonna fall in to that fuckin' fire, someday,' said Annemarie's father on his knees by Granny's side.

Annemarie saw him light the cigarette, placing it carefully between his mother's lips. Then he carried the coffee table over, setting it at her elbow and ordered Annemarie to get an ashtray from the drawer. A smile played across Granny's lips.

Annemarie escaped to examine the bird cage at the window, so the old woman tackled Fat Face hovering near the sofa, 'Sit down and give yer arse a chance.'

The adults laughed; Annemarie didn't. Fat Face plopped her backside down on the faux leather. The couch grumbled under her weight and Granny made a remark about 'breaking every stick of furniture.'

'They must be feedin' you up there anyway,' she said, 'you must be eatin' steady.'

Annemarie waited for Fat Face to speak, to stick up for herself but Fat Face was silent. Instead the clumsy fingers twisted around the fringing of her coat, these fingers that Annemarie had tried and failed to school in the art of French plaiting.

'It's the bars. She does nothing but eat bars and rubbish,' her father said, taking a deep drag on his cigarette.

He puffed out, 'I thought you were on Players . . . the mind to cuttin' down?'

'Aiye but them Players are pure paper. I got him to get forty Benson at the Black man's.'

'Where is he now?'

She smoked leisurely, taking the cigarette out of her mouth and examining it.

'Awh, he's up doing a bit a buildin' work for your brother . . . Tommy needs the extension for the boys'

'The ole boy's not able for that at his age.'

Polly, recognising Annemarie, began to chirp. The budgie was old – no one knew exactly how old, maybe seven maybe eleven – and prone to fits of trilling, today she was quiet.

'Where is Max?'

Granny stirred in her chair.

'He's dead. I told him not to put wet leaves into the cage but he wouldn't listen.'

'Why would Granda do that? He showed me how to look after the birds.'

'Daft bird musta ate one a' them and poisoned himself.'

Annemarie's face closed up. She had to turn quickly back to the window.

The old woman cleared her throat, 'Your father was up with the solicitor.'

Annemarie's father stills the poker.

'Right?'

'Cooney, says he can do the will next week. He says at yer father's age it's as well to get these things sorted.'

'And it's good fer makin him a few poun'.'

She took a raspy breath and let it out in hacks.

'It has to be done ...' she said, still spluttering, 'Yer brother's goin' to sort out the bill... yi know seein' as he'll be gettin' the house an' all.'

Then she hoisted her weight on to the arm-rests.

'Tea?'

From the kitchen, she called about 'queen-buns or biscuits, a sandwich?' and brought everything in on a tray, her slippers shuffling across the lino. A box of white and navy design lay to one side of the tray.

She handed Annemarie the unopened deck of playing cards, 'Here, that'll keep yis busy.'

Fat Face demurred when offered the sugary treats. Annemarie slid onto the sofa beside her and snatched an iced bun. She felt her sister's envious gaze and took pleasure from it, picking the white icing off, feeding each fleck in to her mouth with precision.

Her father rubbed his temples, rasping at the skin with his yellowed fingers. Something had upset him.

He barked at her suddenly from across the room making her jump, 'Watch! Look at the fuckin' mess yer makin' on the floor.'

Annemarie glanced down; perhaps two crumbs had escaped.

Granny, Annemarie concluded, knew how to steady him. She appeared with a bottle and poured a long stream of whiskey into his teacup. It could've been a bottle of milk. Annemarie watched him tear in to it. She put the scalped bun back on the plate.

Granny rambled on about nothing. Time passed. Annemarie could hear Fat Face's stomach rumbling. The chatter rolled on like the words of some strange nursery rhyme. Annemarie was sick of her winning streak. *How many hands of snap can you play in a row?*

'Do you even know how to play twenty-five?' she'd challenged Fat Face and pulled the cards off her sister before she could answer, 'I'll deal.'

When Annemarie had won – again – she scanned the room and noticed her father was resting back, his eyes half closed. The bottle at Granny's side had little more than a finger width left. As if on cue the Belleek clock chimed out the hour, Granny's tale faded conveniently to its conclusion.

'I'd better make a move,' he said.

Annemarie had a feeling that she'd just seen a play acted out.

Granny got up kneading her gnarled hands along her calves, 'Time you were spittin' in yer own ashes.'

At the door Annemarie sensed what was coming next.

'Give yer Granny, a hug,' he ordered.

Fat Face shrank back. Annemarie saw that she would have to lead the way, and went over to press her cheek against the old woman's. She bent down and inhaled the smell of tobacco, and whiskey and caught the high notes of Yardley Lace, rising. The embrace was brief and not altogether unpleasant. Then it was Fat face's turn. Annemarie felt awkward watching. Almost free, Granny seized Fat Face around the shoulder blades rolling the fat across them.

'Yer far too heavy . . . my God the size of ya!' she exclaimed, from the dark little cave of her mouth.

Granny didn't wave them off. She was back in her chair with the snooker turned up loud.

*   *   *

Annemarie and Fat Face were tossed wildly in the backseat; the springs had gone and at speed rear passengers got what Annemarie called the 'bouncy castle' effect. It was strangely exhilarating, but they'd taken Denise – Annemarie's one friend – to see the rock-pools last summer and she'd puked everywhere. Annemarie had the stomach for it and never got car sick, anymore.

Annemaire found it impossible to settle. She couldn't hear Kylie over the noise of the road and she hated Granny for it. She'd upset Annemarie's father talking on and on about Tommy and now the rage was on him and now he was driving scary fast.

Everyone knew her father lost the head when his brother was mentioned. Annemarie imagined her mother giving Fat Face their house – no chance – not with her Sindy collection or the new Bambi tea-set. Annemarie would fight Fat Face for it.

The cat, sitting in the middle of the road, thought he owned the world. He crouched slightly to the left; his squat head and neck tucked into his shoulders in contemplation. Anncmarie would swear the car's front wheel was actually on his tail when her father cut to the right.

The sudden action threw the car off balance. It swung away over to the other side of the road, the back end slashing to and fro across the loose stones. Annemarie gripped the front seat and held her breath. She looked at him pawing the wheel back to his own side.

A jeep behind decided to overtake. Encrusted with muck and dung it hugged the blue car's bumper pressing them on around the bend. Her father's face turned sour. Annemarie saw him raise the bad finger to its driver. When the white lines on the road where broken up like lego the jeep man pulled out.

Annemarie let go of the seat in relief.

A shadow fell across her – the jeep had drawn level, blocking out the light with its high sides. The man's mouth was moving, warping under the tension of curses. Annemarie's vest stuck to the small of her back.

Over the hill a green car was coming. The jeep driver had to go on. Blasting onward with a terrific noise he pumped his big farmer's fist in the air, as if in her father's face. *Why did he have to do that?* An itching crept up Annemarie's spine.

'Ignorant cunt.'

The words exploded in the car.

Her father never let anybody cheek him.

He ground up through the gears, the sound of it making the bun icing turn in her stomach. They were tight up to the jeep. Annemarie wanted to scream because they were about to hit the tow bar. Her father was going to try to pass him on the narrow twisty bit of the road.

Red lights flashed from the jeep, it was slowing, pulling off on to a side road.

Her father had to stamp hard on the brake to avoid him. Effing and blinding he drove in a mad rage. Annemarie puffed in and out with relief, like a horse after being raced. She noticed the quiver in Fat Face's cheek with annoyance and stuck her own balled fists under her thighs.

*   *   *

The sky was still overcast. Gusts got up and toyed with the street debris mixing empty Tayto packets, cigarette butts and plastic bags with crunchy fallen leaves. It began to spit the rain on the way home.

There was a man standing unsteadily on the kerb of lower main-street the wind catching at his dark overcoat. Even if he'd been a stranger to Annemarie, his type was familiar enough. He had just staggered out of the betting shop.

She pleaded inwardly that her father wouldn't see him; she needed to pee, she needed to go home, but they were blocked, now, behind the butcher's van.

Her father rolled the window down and shouted in good humour, 'Dolla, ya ole' cunt have ya lost every penny on the nags?'

'Wee Dam . . . Damien,' he hiccoughed, stifling the regurgitation bubbling in his throat.

Annemarie watched the butcher's man grunt a whole side of cow on to his shoulder. The fleshy ribcage, sawn-in-half, reminded her of the hull of a boat she'd seen at a museum; it leaked crimson on to the man's white overcoat. She thought on Fat Face devouring four sausages in a sitting. She'd managed to put her off black pudding, though. Even Fat Face couldn't stomach the blood and guts poured in to it.

The road cleared. Her father had to go on. Past the post office and up MacBride's lane he kept the Escort moving and stopped, abruptly, in the Church car park.

'Aren't we goin' home, Dad?'

Annemarie dreaded his answer.

He was bound to know it wasn't right – bringing two children to a pub in the middle of the afternoon. But he couldn't stop himself. Dolla was the problem. It seemed to Annemarie that he lured her father there deliberately.

It stank, it was dark and Annemarie hated it. When the yeasty scent of a fresh barrel hit he became an altered man, no longer her father. She was hurriedly installed with Fat Face at a window table; then abandoned for the bar. One other patron sucked a pipe in the corner. The bar man thumped a glass on the counter. Annemarie noticed her father's movements were slower. What, she wondered, was he waiting for when he swirled the orange liquid twice before sipping?

'Throw it in to ya,' said Dolla, zipping himself up as he emerged from the back door, 'I'm buyin.'

She saw that the great form of the morning was restored in him. Two pints and another whiskey appeared – Dolla had started the fattening. Her father slapped his patron on the back, showing his appreciation by downing the half neat.

Annemarie listened to the talk of a cute-hoor farmer, caught by the tax-man. She and Fat Face eyed each other across the round table, sharing the same thought, *'How are we to get him out of here?'*

Her father was trapped and she and Fat Face were imprisoned with him.

Slowfox

Kerri Ward

'I can't remember,' he says.

The room is loud and packed with moving bodies. The instructor is hollering the time signature out over the music and rubber-soled shoes squeak occasionally on the floorboards. We're not supposed to wear that kind of shoe – they make you stick to the floor, don't let you move around easily enough. But we're only the beginner class, so I guess it doesn't matter so much what shoes we're wearing yet.

We're the only people not dancing. We're standing very still in the middle of the floor. A husband and wife much older and better than us are getting close, and I pull Martin over to the side of the room so we don't cause a pile-up. His jaw is set so hard he would look really angry, frightening even, to another person. But I know it's just because he feels embarrassed.

'What part don't you remember?' I say gently. 'Maybe I can jog your memory.'

'None of it,' he says, staring at his feet. He has his Dad's old black Oxfords on. I insisted we both wear proper shoes for dancing, and our best clothes. I don't like doing things by halves. I don't really see the point.

'Well, we did this one last week,' I say as another couple, who look like they're in their mid-sixties, swing gracefully past us. 'It's the waltz. You start on your left foot, stepping forward, because you're the leader, and I start on my right, stepping back, because I'm the follower, and it goes one-two-three, one-two-three…'

I tap out the rhythm on the back of his hand. He looks up at me and his eyes are total blanks. So I lead him back onto the floor, even though I'm not supposed to be leading anyone anywhere – I should *only* be following, as the instructor has already reminded us – and I lift his hands back into the waltz hold and step in close and say, 'Okay, I'll count us in and we'll just do the basic step a few times. Just watch my feet and do the same, but in reverse, alright?'

But just as we do the first few steps, the music ends. The instructor comes on the mic and tells us to do a 'big finish', and some of the leaders twirl their partners around. Martin doesn't twirl me. He's still staring down at his feet like he's worried they're plotting against him.

Everybody claps and then goes to change their shoes and pick up their jackets. The advanced class are waiting outside. I dawdle for a few minutes over putting my trainers on so I can watch them. The instructor puts on a song and says 'okay, advanced class, let's warm up with the foxtrot!' and they all glide into position on the dancefloor and start moving together like it's as natural as breathing. It's breathtaking just watching them, but Martin is getting impatient to go, so I grab my coat and we walk out into the long hallway lined with lockers and notices for bake sales and babysitters and French classes. Then, just as we reach the exit, I hear the instructor calling my name. He runs up after us, clutching something in his hands.

'Well,' he says, a bit out of breath, 'did you find it okay tonight? Did you enjoy yourselves?'

He's grinning so much it's a bit creepy. Martin goes all quiet and just sort of nods, but I do my best to smile back.

'It was really great,' I say. 'I think we're getting there with the waltz. Just need a little more practice, right?'

'Of course!' he says, and he runs a hand over his very well-coiffed hair. It's always perfect, and I can't help wondering what he uses to keep it in place like that. 'I think you're both doing wonderfully. I just wanted to mention that you're always welcome to come along to the other beginner classes during the week, if you think you need some extra practice. That is, I mean, if you would like.' He shuffles his feet. 'Don't over-exert yourself, obviously, you're doing great – you'll pick it all up easy enough. But if you want more time … well, what I mean to say is – the offer is there.'

Martin is looking at the instructor as if his perfect hair has caught fire. I'm not sure what to say, so I mumble some kind of thank you and say that of course, we'd love that, we'll be along during the week for a little extra practice. Then the instructor thrusts what he's been clutching into my hands and says,

'It seems to be raining pretty hard out there, so please, take my umbrella.'

The foxtrot music has ended and he says goodbye very quickly and then dashes back inside. Martin pulls the door open for me and we step outside. I don't think the rain is very heavy at all, but Martin makes me put up the instructor's little black umbrella and then walks very close to me until we get home.

Around midnight I vomit and that starts a nosebleed. I leave Martin asleep and go sit on the toilet with my head tipped forward and a handful of kitchen roll pressed over my face. About ten minutes later Martin wakes up and when he sees me he gets so angry he kicks the bathroom door, and I have to ask him to calm down because it doesn't help, when he gets like that. I'm afraid he'll do something stupid and hurt himself, so I ask him to get me the ice pack and more kitchen towel and make us both a cup of chamomile tea. He seems calmer when he comes back and helps me apply the ice pack to the bridge of my nose. I show him that the bleeding is really light, just a tiny trickle, and of course I'd have woken him if I thought it was a hospital emergency. I want to tell him that not *everything* is a hospital emergency, but honestly, he wouldn't believe me if I did.

I don't want to move into the living room in case I bleed on the carpet so we stay in the bathroom and Martin sits on the floor beside me. We're both very quiet and the only sound is the extractor fan quietly whirring above us.

'I'm sorry I'm so crap at this dancing thing,' he says, after a long while.

'You're not crap,' I say.

'I am,' he replies. 'It's been nearly a month and I can't even remember the basics.'

'These things take time,' I say, and that just hangs for a bit.

'What was the name of that dance you wanted to learn?' he asks.

'The slowfox. It's supposed to be the most difficult ballroom dance to learn – a bit like the foxtrot, but way harder. I've watched loads of videos and I can't follow it at all. But it just looks *amazing*. Really smooth and graceful, like ice skating.'

'Have you done that yet? Ice skating?' Martin asks suddenly, and he seems excited.

'Well, no, but I think that would be … you know.' *Too risky,* I mean, but I don't want to say it out loud.

It goes quiet again. The ice pack has turned my hands numb. I lift it away and realise the blood has run through the kitchen towel and soaked into my t-shirt. I grab a wad of tissue and try not to let Martin see. I start counting how many minutes it's been.

'We can go to the extra lessons, if you like,' he says quietly, looking at his bare feet. 'I'm sure I'll improve with the extra practice. It's just not enough really, an hour a week, to get the hang of it.'

'Martin…'

'No, honestly. We can go any day that you feel up to it. And we can ask the instructor to show us the slowfox this week, to maybe speed things up a bit –'

'No, it's not that,' I say, and I try to get up, but the toilet seat is slippery and I can't get a grasp on it, and it's getting a bit hard to breathe and there's that rushing feeling in my head. 'I mean – I think it's a hospital emergency now.'

My left nostril was cauterised a month ago, and now it's the right nostril's turn. At least they match. They take some blood samples first and then after the procedure is over they bring us up to the inpatient ward, which makes my stomach twist. We sit down in a waiting room full of ugly, padded green chairs and wait. The only other person there is a middle-aged man in stripy pyjamas reading a paperback in another language. He looks up and examines my face, then stands up and shuffles back to his room. A nurse I've never seen before whose name is Maya comes to tell me that the procedure went just fine but the tests say I'm anaemic and I'll need a blood transfusion.

'Do you know what that means?' she asks, writing notes in my file. I know it's my file because it's two folders, one red and one brown, held together with a big orange rubber band. I always check to make sure that they have the right file, because you hear stories.

'I have to stay overnight,' I try to say, but my voice dissolves into nothing because my nose is still numb and prickly.

'You'll have to stay with us overnight,' Maya says cheerfully in that slightly-too-loud voice. 'So we'll get you into a bed and get you nice and comfy and then you'll be feeling better in no time.' She flicks though a sheaf of papers that look like test results. 'You sure must have been feeling tired today, am I right? Your haemoglobin is only six. What was it last time, do you know?'

Martin shoots me a sideways look that I refuse to meet.

'I can't remember,' I say, but my voice is just a squeak. Maya makes a sympathetic face, that kind of sideways half-smile and furrowed brow that they all do.

'It's ok, I can look it up on the system later. Your next day ward appointment is Thursday morning, right? You're showing early signs of thrombocytopenia, so I think we may need to do a platelet transfusion.

We could schedule that in before your chemo. Or after, if you prefer, though that might not be a great idea if you usually vomit afterwards...'

She writes down a few things and checks a few others. She asks me all the usual questions. My chest feels tight and hard, like a balloon that's been overinflated. Like it might burst. Maya checks her clippy nurse's watch and stands up.

'Your bed should be ready soon,' she says, smiling at us. 'I'll come and get you in a bit.' She looks at Martin. 'Did you want to stay?' she asks, a little hesitant.

'Yes,' he answers. 'I mean, if that's okay.'

When we're alone, Martin puts his hand on my hand and squeezes it twice. Outside, on the ward, I can hear a nurse doing rounds, swinging the doors open and then closed, her shoes squeaking on the polished lino. My whole face feels prickly and hot.

'Well, that wasn't so bad,' Martin says eventually. 'It could have been worse.'

'This is my fault,' I say, gritting my teeth. 'I'm so stupid. Thinking we could go dancing. Thinking *I* could do something like that.' I crush my fists into my eyeballs because I want to cry, even though it would make my nose hurt, and even though it would upset Martin, and even though I always say that there's no point in crying about it because tears don't fix anything. I keep pressing hard on them until I see spots and the tight feeling in my chest starts to loosen, and then I sigh loudly and stare at my feet.

'I don't know,' Martin says. 'I'm not sure what the doctor would say. Maybe you shouldn't be dancing.' He pauses. 'But I think if you want to, you probably should.'

'I do,' I say, but then I stop. 'But I'm not sure why. I mean, I never wanted to do it until I started treatment. I guess it's something I never thought we could do ... but that doesn't seem to matter so much any more. It would be nice to be able to do something physical again. You know – something that's challenging.'

Martin laughs, and it's so loud and unexpected that I jump.

'Right,' he says, nodding. 'Like this isn't challenging enough.' And that makes me kind of smile.

Then Maya's head pops around the corner. 'We're ready for you now, Tom,' she says.

I wake up a couple of hours into the transfusion because Martin is tapping me on the arm.

'Are you still here?' I say, wincing because the anaesthetic has worn off and now my nose hurts like hell.

'You were trying to pull the line out,' he says, pointing to my chest port. He's sitting in a visitor's chair by the bed with his earphones in and his phone in his lap. 'You must have been having a nightmare.'

'I was dreaming about dancing,' I say, trying not to move my nose too much when I speak.

Somewhere in the room a man coughs loudly. The lights are still dim. I check my phone – it's just after five a.m.

'You shouldn't still be here,' I say as sternly as I can with the pain. 'You have work in a few hours.'

Martin shrugs.

'I'm serious,' I say, and normally I would have continued with *there's no sense in you running yourself into the ground too,* and *someone has to pay the bills,* and *you need to look after yourself more.* Instead I say, 'do I hear music?'

Martin pulls out his earphones and hands me his phone.

'I've been watching some videos,' he says.

On the screen two tiny figures, a man in a tux and a woman in a red dress, glide across a vast, gleaming floor in the opening figure of the slowfox. The tinny sound of a jazz band filters through the earphones as they and spin and dip in time with the music.

'It would have to be a bit different, I guess, the way we would do it,' he says, pulling his chair around so he's sitting beside me. 'But I found something else, too.' He taps on the screen and a video pops up titled *Annual Same-Sex Ballroom Dancing Competition, A Class: Waltz.*

'There's this competition in Holland somewhere,' he says, and the light from the screen makes his eyes shine. Four couples in sweeping gowns and extravagant sequined tuxes take their places together on a ballroom floor – men with men and women with women. 'So we could even compete. You know, eventually. When you're better.'

Somewhere in the room someone makes a shushing sound. Martin ignores it.

'And look,' he says, standing up and shuffling over until his back is up against the curtain. He holds his arms up awkwardly and stares down at his feet. He takes one stiff step forward on the right foot, then a side step with the left foot, then brings his right foot over to join it. A single basic waltz figure. He looks up at me.

'Well?' he says.

'You started on the wrong foot,' I say. 'But that was good. Really good.'

'It's an improvement,' he says. And for a second he just stands there, looking at me, his arms still frozen in a waltz hold.

'It's a nice idea,' I say. 'But let's be honest with ourselves. We'll never go further than beginner's lessons. We'll never be able to compete in a competition like that.'

'Why not?' Martin asks, his arms falling to his sides. 'Why couldn't we?'

'Because you're rubbish at this dancing thing,' I say, and that makes him laugh.

'I love you,' he says, very quietly.

I start laughing then, too. I laugh until my eyes are streaming, and Martin has to come and put his arms around my shoulders and hold me very tightly, because now the tears have started it feels like they might never stop.

The Godsend

Emma Devlin

Margaret still walked as tall and as straight as she had that morning, even now as the first few stars appeared behind the clouds, and her brother sank low on her shoulder. The mists of the afternoon were turning into evening rain, still so light that the drops seemed to be rising from the ground. For all their lightness they stuck to her; the scarf around her head was already soaked. For the past hour Owen had let himself lean harder and harder against her, just about putting one foot in front of the other. He was not heavy enough, though, to slow her down.

'I'm hungry,' Owen said, 'Can we stop now?'

'You stop now, you won't start again.'

They had been walking since dawn, and she didn't want them to stop now, not now, when tomorrow afternoon, or even before, would bring them up into the hills, to the lights of their destination. She meant what she'd said: Owen was hard to rouse in the mornings, and could barely walk alone. Not her, though, who was practically walking for him. She had always been stronger, and meaner, than him, though she had been born too early. Where Owen had been born late, after week upon week of a dull thudding in his mother's belly, Margaret had come down on her in a dozen tight knuckles of pain, demanding to come out then and there in the fields, dusting the ground with both their blood. She was hungry now thinking of the potatoes that had grown in those fields: nourished, she could pretend, with her own blood, growing the bigger and fatter for it, until one year, when she was fifteen, and her brother was twelve, what they dug up was blackened and soft, then again, then again. Then came not just hunger, but daily emptiness, and weakness, and away went their parents, planted back into the fields by Owen and Margaret before they were forced to leave. The only thing Owen had taken for himself was their father's old folding knife. There was nothing much else to take.

'I'm hungry, though,' Owen said again. Margaret, without stopping, pulled out the parcel of food she had tucked into her skirts: old roots, nettle leaves, acorns, seeds. Whatever she could scrounge. Not much of it. Whatever was good on the road was already gone. She hoped that they would arrive at the place before their food was gone. If not, they would eat the cloth their food was wrapped in, and after that she might have to take the scarf from her head and eat that too. After that, she didn't know. She took an acorn out of the pack for Owen and he ate it without complaint. It had ceased to amaze them how easily they ate these things. The misty sheets of rain turned slowly into fat drops of water as they walked. She felt heavy in her wools and homespuns, though she was empty, empty, empty inside.

'We'll get something proper soon,' she said. 'Haven't I always found us a place to eat?'

At first Margaret had tried to steer them down the paths and roads she remembered from days out with her mother and father, until one day she found them on a path she hardly recognised, and then another, going further and further away from home until she remembered nothing, and decided that the only thing to do was walk. Walk, and feed themselves, in that order. She told herself that it was her own common sense, not just good fortune, which had seen them walk into town after town: where there were walls, there were people; where there were well kept hedges, there had been people. She told herself that she could read these things, even when that list grew smaller and smaller, and more desperate. Her directions, this time, came from a man she'd spoken to at the soup kitchen in the last town. He had sat on the ground clutching his now-empty bowl, as if he could will it to be full again. They were closing the kitchens, he'd said. That soup they'd just been given was the last serving, as though tomorrow morning they'd wake up with full stomachs again. If there was soup in the next town, it wasn't for them. Margaret had let Owen sleep while she went and spoke with the man about the other place. He'd told her how to find it, though he himself could not bear the thought of rising and following them there. Follow the coastal path, he'd said, pointing. It was longer that way, but the fresh air was better than the dark, stale vapours of the forest, where those sick with hunger were known to fall and die as they walked. She wouldn't tell Owen. Tired and little as he'd become, it was hard enough to hold him upright as he tried to walk. She didn't think even she had the strength to drag him.

Their path took them over a worn track beaten out of the grass by countless other feet. That, then, was the sign, even if the hedges here were untended and creeping towards the path: those feet must have gone somewhere. She followed this track it opened out across a bare rock face, leaving them exposed to the open sea, whose peat-coloured waters, in tight waves, pulled at the stones below. Owen pointed at something, and Margaret screwed up her face against the rain.

'Look!' There was a lone figure further down the path, whose giant coat obscured its form, man or woman. Margaret could see that the figure was facing them, waiting for them to approach. She felt Owen tug at her, but Margaret kept her pace. However much she hated taking them there, they had to eat. When it got dark, the old man had told her, she would see the workhouse lights on the hill above the road. They were close, though she didn't know how far was still to go. The stars were rising, she was fixed on the hills, and she wouldn't stop. As they drew closer to the figure, Margaret could see that it was a woman, whose frieze coat was for someone taller and wider than herself. Margaret's own clothes, even in the damp, did enough to keep her warm. Owen, though, shivered and chattered his teeth at night as he slept, and could use a fine thick coat like that. The strange woman waved at them as they approached, as though she were an old friend.

'I was just about to give up, when I saw you coming.' The woman smiled at them as she spoke. She, unlike the others they had passed on the road, still had a little red to her cheeks, though her thinness had almost sunk beneath the bones. All rosy and light to Margaret and Owen's brown and pallor.

'We never saw you at all, until now,' Margaret replied.

'Being hungry does that. You can't think much, or see.'

'I've heard that.'

'Aren't you hungry, then?'

Margaret began to walk again. 'Like everyone else,' she said as she passed the woman. 'We can't stop, I'm sorry.'

'Would you like some meat? I have bread.'

Owen pulled on Margaret's arm and forced her to turn. 'You have meat?'

'Who has meat out here? Who can afford anything?' the woman replied. 'You take what you find. *If* you can go and get it.' She stepped towards the ledge and gestured at the coast below.

Margaret tried to pull Owen forwards again, but found he pulled back with a strength she hadn't seen from him in days. 'Move. She's talking nonsense. There's nothing out here. Owen, come *on*.'

'See for yourself,' the woman said.

Owen slipped away from Margaret and joined the woman. He looked down to where the shore met the seam of the rock wall. 'Come and see, Margaret!'

She followed him and looked. There was, lying on its side, jammed between the rocks and the cliff, the carcass of whale, turned by some defect from grey to the colour of a linen shirt. Seabirds had gathered on the surrounding rocks in droves, though the woman threw a stone at them to drive them away.

'I've only seen a living whale once in my life,' the woman said. 'When I was a child. They drove it up the river and killed it. What they didn't eat they sold.'

'We've only seen pictures,' murmured Owen.

'We can't buy anything from you,' Margaret said. 'We haven't any money.' Truthfully, looking at the whale, she felt hunger blooming deep inside her, such as she had been ignoring for weeks.

'I know you don't. Go and bring me some back. I have a little bread. I'd go down myself, only I'm afraid of the birds. If I fell I'd shatter. I'm too old. Bring some back for me, and some for yourself. Eat it, sell it. Whatever you like.' The woman could only be a handful of years older than Margaret, and there was something in the way she bobbed up and down on her feet, in her brightness, that Margaret disliked.

Margaret looked at Owen. He was still looking down at the whale. 'I have the knife,' he said. 'I could go down.'

'That's lucky,' The woman laughed. 'But you? You're that small you'd be down there for days. You go,' she said to Margaret.

'How –?'

'Just cut and pull and bring back what comes out.'

'I'm hungry,' Owen muttered. 'I'll go.'

'You will not,' said Margaret. 'You haven't the strength for it.' She paused. 'Give me the knife.' She stepped closer, and when he passed her the knife she stuffed their food into his pocket.

'I'll go,' she said to the woman. 'If you give me that coat for my brother.'

'Done. Go!' the woman said, clapping her hands. 'Just cut and pull, and bring back what comes out.'

Margaret looked down. The cliff face wasn't as steep as she'd thought, with rocks piled up against it in roughshod little leaps and steps. She picked out a way down that would curve towards the sea first, across the beach, and back up. The knife was too bulky to tuck into her skirts, so she held it awkwardly in one hand as she climbed down.

Occasionally she lost sight of the whale as she scrambled through the creases between the rocks, but there was always the sight and smell of the birds to remind her where to find it.

She considered the knife: would it be enough? It had a dark, wooden handle which hid a long, cold looking blade. Her father had only ever used it on ropes and tough branches, and even though Owen had managed to keep it sharp, she didn't know how it would take to flesh. What resistance, anyway, would the whale give her? She'd heard words like 'blubber' before, which in her mind was a bubbling, grey material under a hide as thick as treacle, into which things sank and were never released. She stopped herself from thinking that way. The animal, seen from below, had looked as limp and as soft as any fish pulled from the water. It was hard to believe it could be of the same character as those whales she had seen pictures of, throwing themselves upwards and backward, head to tail, and smashing the sea to bits around them. Smaller, too, she thought, and somehow she could picture the knife going in easier, sliding through its body as easily as if she were cutting felt. Meat, finally: cooked, cut up over bread, and – why not? – mixed with what was left with their own roots and leaves. Enough of it to last them until they reached the workhouse. The realisation hit her suddenly, almost made her lose her footing, it was so staggering. Enough of it and they could walk past the workhouse straight into town, as though she'd always meant to go there. Owen would never know. Enough of it, and if it kept, they could sell it, and buy their way off the road. She found herself moving faster now, shooing away the birds that grew more numerous the closer she got. She stank of stagnant puddles, rain, and seawater, and something else, but she didn't mind. Her mouth was already watering, not just for the food itself, but for everything else. She had heard of people leaving for America, where, to hear them tell it, everything they wanted would fall on them from the sky. A New World, people had once called it, still called it sometimes, and she imagined that a young place like that would be a vibrant, waxy thing, covered in crops yet unpicked, untouched by blight. Why not? She would take them straight past the workhouse and into the town, then past the town and onto a boat. She would get the money. People had done it already. Those feet had all gone somewhere. She wanted that.

The smell grew stronger as she approached the creature. She recognised it, somehow. She thought it was herself, then the birds, then knew it was the whale. The smell made her think of her potatoes, blackened, turning to liquid in her hands, and of the day their mother passed, then their father, and the days she and Owen had spent burying them in those rotten fields. Her stomach boiled. Rot. The animal was rotting from the bottom up, spilling its insides, and its oils, over the rocks, into the water lapping around it, to be fought over by the birds. She hadn't seen it from up on the ledge. Too hungry to see properly, like the woman had said.

Margaret walked over to the whale and, without knowing why, smoothed the water off what was left of the whale's head, leaving the imprints of her palm on the thin flesh around its jaws. She didn't want to cry over it. Her throat was sore. She examined the body. There wasn't much meat on the whale now, and nothing to eat, not even the eyes, despite the size of the wreck left behind. She was hungrier than she had been in weeks. She picked up a pebble and swung it towards the birds, trying, this time, to hit one. She grabbed at them as they flew past her, hoping to wring a neck or tear a wing. Whale meat, bird meat, anything. They slipped past her unfamiliar, clumsy hands. She would go back up, all the way back up that cliff, with nothing of the whale on her but the smell.

The climb back up exhausted her. Approaching the top, she called to Owen to help her, but he didn't reply. She continued on. Her mind was blank. She was soaking, grey from head to toe, and beginning to freeze. The hunger, awoken in earnest by the promise of meat, was tugging downwards at her. She would have loved to simply stop, and lie down, and let Owen drag himself the rest of the way. But she didn't stop. Finally she pulled herself over the ledge, onto her knees, her arms trembling with the effort. She didn't see Owen at first, until he called out to her weakly. He was on the ground, some distance away from the path, one hand planted heavily on the ground, the other covering his eye. She hurried over to him.

'She robbed me,' he said. 'When you were out of sight.'

Margaret crouched beside him. 'What did she do?'

'She hit me.' He took his hand away. There was already a red and violet mark around his eye. His voice broke. 'She took the food. I didn't have anything else, so she just took it.'

'The food?' Margaret said. 'What food?' She laughed; it came out in a choke. 'It was just acorns and leaves, Owen.' The path ahead was strewn with fallen things from their pack, even the discarded cloth itself, all crushed and trampled into the dirt. 'I bet she was disappointed in us.'

'She bolted. We don't even know her name.'

Her hands were empty. 'I lost the knife,' Margaret realised suddenly, laughing harder. 'I must have dropped it.'

'That was father's knife.'

'She didn't even leave you her coat,' and Margaret roared with laughter.

'No meat,' Owen said finally, quietly, and that finally made her stop. Margaret took a deep breath and pulled him to his feet. After the effort of the climb, even he felt heavy. He looked at her, his good eye large and wet, waiting for her to speak. Margaret looked away. Her mind stirred. Run down the path and catch the woman. Take her bread, until she realised that even the bread was probably a lie. Take the coat then, or her boots, or anything else, even her clothes, her hair. Go back for the knife and run after her. Go back to the whale and eat it anyway, let the rot kill them both. She thought these things until she felt light-headed and nearly fell on Owen.

'What do we do?' he asked.

Margaret didn't speak. She took his arm and pulled him forwards, looking up at the hills. She thought she saw a small figure moving in the darkness, running, and she thought she'd crack in half, until she blinked and the figure was gone. The last of her resolve vanished with it, if it was ever there at all. Below them was the clatter of dozens of birds circling the body of the whale. She could still smell it. She led Owen forward, towards the hills, where overheard she had spotted the first of the yellow candle lights of the workhouse.

Dirty Playing Cards

Peter Alexander Arden

The brightness and the hot bus trawl Darren was used to. Last year
they'd been to Lanzarote, this year Fuerteventura. So for two hours
his head lolled and bumped dozily into things, but it didn't bother him
as much as it might. His dad snored beside him, bent in over his belly.
The cosy weight of him asleep in a chair only a little more familiar
than the sight of his vest, or the straggly hairs on his upper arms. In the
V-gap between the bus-seats his mum panted and swigged water: her
usual response to summer. His brother, even though he was bigger than
she was already, crowded her space as well as his own, draping over
her like a lion over a warm rock. No surprise there. The white-washed
towns he recognised well. The rattly roads and black volcanic earth.
Last year they saw a geyser shoot steam like a whale does water. Not
that he'd seen a whale ever, yet. There were too the customary couple of
interesting girls. He spied one slight cute one a couple of seats up with
a Buffy-like upturned nose and straightened grey-sky hair. While the
men clamoured unbundling luggage at the drop-off point he overheard
her arguing with her little sister and her mum, and she spoke with a
lovely Scottish lilt despite the frustration in her tone. She seemed about
his age, but it was hard to tell. The other girl of note was a pale black-
laced goth who, it turned out, lived less than two miles from where they
did at home. Their mums remarked in the lobby how funny it was they
had never met before, but the same thing happened last year twice, and

twice more with people they did know. Kenny, his brother, was that bit older, taller, stronger; the goth girl barely batted her dark eyes in Darren's direction. The echoey apartment complex, two stories built around a wobbly-shaped pool, was great but not too new. And that all those holidaying were white, while all the workers black, was simply matter of course. People from other countries often looked different and besides, Darren enjoyed the change. Which is, perhaps, why his surprise, though arousing, was mild, when he felt the wild, wholly unusual urge to fuck his apartment's cleaning lady. Not that he'd fucked anyone ever, yet, either.

* * *

The urge arrived as she did, on the second day in.
Darren's mum sizzled by the pool. His dad drank beer and read in the shade of their apartment across the pool. He and Kenny were inside their apartment with the blinds drawn against the blinding heat. Kenny was doing press-ups with his feet on the sofabed while Darren rocked on the edge, enjoying *Windwaker* on the small square tv. He was midway through a ramble, 'it's cool… feels like I'm on the boat. The colours are so– full of joy. I can't stop smiling. Look how– blue the ocean; that's my favourite blue. And the animay-' when there was a solid series of bangs on the door. Barely had the sullen, muffled, 'hell-o, cleaning,' reached Darren's peaked ears before she burst in and bent over and shove-kicked a doorstop under the door. She had wide hips, fully filled her oddly-formal uniform and her thick hair was tight-bound in a bushy bun. Pressed he would have guessed she was his mum's age, and size – that is, 40 and fat – but she was black and carried her weight well. It was hard to tell.

Kenny puffed and stood up, downed half a stubby beer. He whispered, 'right, I'm away out here to… sniff around,' and sidled out the gap in the sliding doors.

Darren paused the game.

He idled in the inventory and kept the cleaner in the corner of his eye. She wasn't attractive in a way he understood, but it didn't seem to matter. He felt the urge: a wild desire to run up and stick his –. She was powerful. She stomped open the flip-lid bin. Snatched at the empty ice-cream wrappers on the counter. The toilet roared as she thrust down the handle.

Darren went outside.

The goth girl smoked in the shade, giving away glances at Kenny. He stood with his back to her, struggling to draw a conversation from their dad.

His mum squinted from her deck-chair, 'what's wrong hunny bun?'

The coddling tone upset him further. '*Nothing*,' he groaned.

'I have some of your men in my bag.'

'The cleaner is in our apartment.'

'Well leave her alone. And leave me too, grumpy bum, you're blockin' my sun.'

Darren stood over the pool. He leaned forward like a falling plank, letting the water give him a good stinging slap. He blew some air from his lungs so he could squat at the bottom. When he resurfaced his mum whined, 'you're a wee get, I'm *soaked.*'

'I didn't mean to. Where's my men?'

He played for an hour or so with his GI Joes, creating histories and reasons, engaging in elaborate fight sequences. Cooling down. Once his shoulders tired and tingled from the sun he climbed from the pool and waddled back to the apartment, checking it was empty before sidling in and dropping his florid three-quarter-lengths splat on the tiles. About a month before the holiday, Darren had found a set of dirty playing cards under the driver's seat of his dad's car. Now he rooted around his suitcase for the sock he'd hidden them in. Full frontal, big-breasted, bushy-vaginaed women. Jackpot. He masturbated. It helped. For about ten minutes.

But he wasn't to see the cleaner again for several days. There was little within walking distance of their complex but black rock and further apartments. During the day his family dragged him to coastal towns, to water parks, to markets.

In the evenings after dinner he sat around the pool with the gaggle of pre- and full-on teens, including the lovely-lilted Scottish girl, whose name he had learned was Nicole. As night-time brought cool air and darkness to many parts of the complex, most parents would call their kids in or sit smoking, drinking, at their doorways and balconies. So, despite the removal of the too-young-to-kiss, privacy was hard to come by; Darren and Nicole rarely had a chance to more than speak after each other in their stiff, paranoid circles.

Kenny and the goth girl, Jennifer, Jenny – Jenny, Darren decided, for no other reason than the rhyme – passed in smaller and smaller circles in their own corner in the shade.

The first step he made toward the cleaner was a simple one: he left the cards out.

The family were having a lazy day. In the morning he leafed his way through *Windwaker's* Forbidden Woods and ate some white rolls and ham. Then he took his time spreading the cards face-up all over his messy bed. When he heard her in the hall he slipped out to the pool and bombed in.

The response was poor. The rest of the apartment clean, tidy; the bedroom untouched.

The turn of the week Darren spent jumping into weak waves at the beach. To get the sand off when he got back he jumped into the pool. And later, when two slim blonde English boys emerged from the weekly holidaying reshuffle and began circling Nicole and her sister, Darren jumped back into *Windwaker* too.

Kenny came in late with a grin all over his face.

'Yo.'

'Hi.'

'Holy fuck you're red.'

'I've been in the sun.'

'Here, guess what I just did?'

'I don't know – did you–?'

Kenny shoved two rigid fingers under Darren's nose.

'Sniff those!'

'Don't–' Darren pulled away. 'Actually, that's not that bad.' He sniffed the fingers again. 'It's better than Shannon Samuels.'

'Oh yeahhhh.'

Darren saved the game and went to bed.

More obvious, Darren decided, early next morning in the pool: he needed to be more obvious. He practiced trying to swim full lengths underwater until Nicole's sister, Emma, plunged in next to him; then she and Darren took turns hurling graceless somersaults and careful dives, splashing about until the pool was usurped by manic kids.

'They want me to chase them in the pool,' Emma said, three kids clinging to her for buoyancy. 'Wanna help?'

The kids dragged her screaming under the water.

'Ack,' Darren said. 'No.'

'Why don't you lay up here beside me,' his mum said, 'and play with your men, while I have a wee doze.'

Darren was addled by dark hot thoughts. He took up his men; Snake Eyes today the hero of choice. But he found he had trouble holding onto a satisfying motive. And it frustrated him, how he could animate no more than two men at a time. They fought listlessly over the sweaty creases of his stomach rolls, drowned heads in the pool at his belly button. A battlefield limping under the sporadic drone of his mum's snores.

Kenny eventually left the apartment after Jenny.

Darren grunted and stretched and stood up. His mum gargled in her sleep.

He sidled into the apartment and slipped his shorts off, stiff from the heat. He pottered about the bathroom, checking the cabinet mirror on tip-toes to see how he looked naked. It was hard to tell. He had red lines across where his stomach muscles should be. His heart kept fluttering. He poked on the GameCube.

Link's little pondering face calmed his nervous surges. His *hups* and his *yips*. In his quest to restore the Triforce, he happily traversed every map-square of the Great Sea, the flooded plains of Hyrule. He docked now at Southern Triangle Island and placed the final pearl, Nayru's Pearl, in the hands of its worried-looking stone guardian. In an epic cut-scene, the Tower of the Gods emerged from beneath the bubbling sea; a huge, dilapidated lighthouse-shaped tower with the shell of a bailey at its base.

The King of Red Lions, the talking boat upon which Link sailed, turned to him and said:

You must rise above the trial of the–

Darren pressed the big green A button to skip the text and get on with the game. He heard a rattling noise. A trolley.

He paused the game and listened. A deep voice.

He darted to the bathroom and turned on the shower, leaving the bathroom door open, the shower curtain drawn to the side. He climbed in and lathered himself up.

A solid series of bangs.

He rubbed at his penis to make it bigger.

'Hell-o, cleaning.'

Darren aimed his hips at the door.

She started. '*Oh*!'

'Shit!'

He belatedly covered himself.

'Sorry!'

She was already in the kitchen, stomping and snatching at things.

Darren turned off the shower and dried himself down and went into his bedroom and sat naked on the bed. The cleaner stayed in the front room. He finally closed his door, and right away she made her way into the bathroom to clean.

Maybe she misread the situation. Maybe she thought she *had* just caught him, by accident, in the shower.

He put on some loose boxers and creaked open the door. She was bent over in the hallway, leaning into the bathroom. Her body emanated pungent sweat like a force-field. He had to think fast. Press the issue. He still had a semi; as he passed into the living room he brushed it up against her bursting rear. Then he picked up his controller and un-paused the game, and she moved on again as if nothing happened, leaving shortly after.

He dove onto his bed and punched his pillow, fought not to cry. He spread the cards out and masturbated and ate some ham rolls and played *Windwaker*.

She didn't appear again at her usual time. Three evenings in a row Darren returned red-faced to an unclean apartment.

On the tenth day of their two-week stay the family went whale watching. Darren gripped the railings on the upper deck of the glass-bottomed boat and squinted excitedly over the ocean, hearing all the while in his mind the drums and the horns of the sailing song in *Windwaker*, straining in search of the mooted gamming sperm whales. For a while a school of dolphins giggled along next to the V and the gushing foam at the front of the boat. The captain slowed to a stop, and a tour guide announced over the radio that anyone who wanted could jump in and swim with the dolphins. Darren ran down to the middle deck, yanking off his t-shirt and his shoes and socks. His dad cheered, '*go an son*,' as he swung over the railings and dove from high into the bracing ocean. But when he emerged dolphins were gone.

He returned in the evening taut, tired, and without a sniff of a whale. Hobbling through the lobby ahead of his puffed parents, his gait recovered miraculously when he noticed the half-shaded pool was empty, save for a set of lovely-lilted feet.

Nicole snorted and cupped her hands over her mouth when Darren described the peak of his whale hunt.

'And Emma said you were good at diving.'

'I'm actually not bad.'

'Well let me see then.'

'Ack.'

'Go on.'

Darren swung his arms and dove into the pool.

Nicole smiled. 'Not bad. Probably should have taken your t-shirt off.'

'It'll dry in no time. See you do better.'

Nicole patted his bobbing head. 'Maybe later,' she said.

'Yo,' Kenny said.

'What?'

'Mum wants to see you in the lobby.'

'Why?'

Nicole squinted. 'Are you wearing eyeliner?'

Kenny's mouth wrenched. 'What? No. Just go see her now,' he said, and left.

Darren waddled into the lobby.

'What am I going to do with you?' his mum said.

'I was in the pool.'

She sighed. 'Come on, this way.'

She led him to the manager's office.

The manager was a slender black man with sunglasses resting on his bald head. Darren fidgeted for comfort on a wicker chair and dripped on the floor.

'Do you know why you're here?' his dad asked.

'Am I – not allowed in the pool with my clothes on?'

The manager crossed his arms and sat back. 'I do not want to push this,' he said, looking at Darren. 'One of my staff has told me that you were –' he struggled for the word.

'Inappropriate,' his mum muttered.

His dad *hmmed*.

'Yes, inappropriate. I have spoken to your mother and father. We wanted to hear what you had to say.'

Darren's voice cracked. He stumbled, 'she came in when I was in the shower the other day, if that's what you–. Is that–? I left the door open, by accident. I didn't think. I – I can't think of anything else that would have… no. I – I don't know.'

Little drips plashing peppered the slow silence.

The manager raised his eyebrows at Darren's dad. 'Like I said, I do not want to – push this.'

All three adults looked at Darren. He looked at the leg of the desk.

'I don't know,' he said again, and shrugged.

*   *   *

Kenny lay back on the sofabed and Darren played *Windwaker.* It was their last night.

'I'm so hungry,' Kenny said.

'Why don't you eat?'

'I'm – I don't wanna bulk up, too much.'

'Is that why you look so pale?'

'She likes to – sit in the shade.'

'Are you her boyfriend now?'

Kenny popped open a stumpy beer and sipped at the rising foam. 'I think so,' he said.

Outside, Darren could see the gaggle gathered by the pool. Emma was there, but not Nicole. It was their last night too.

He was deep in Ganon's Tower. It looked like this was the final battle. The King of Red Lions nodded next to a purple portal and told him that if he wanted to retreat, to go back to the world and recoup before taking on Ganon himself, he could do so here. He already had the Triforce of Courage and a fully-charged Master Sword, but he only 17 hearts out of a possible 20. There was still more to explore, to collect. He didn't know if he was strong enough. It was hard to tell.

Kenny downed another stumpy and said, 'right, I'm away over to...' and ducked out.

Darren decided to retreat. Save the game.

He ambled to the pool. The doorways and balconies were less populated than usual due to the last minute packing taking place in half the rooms. The added seclusion lending a sense of expectation to the already strained atmosphere. Everybody stood about not meeting eyes.

One of the English boys said to a pudgy girl in a dress, 'do you want to go for a walk?' She nodded and they walked away side by side. This happened three or four times. Darren wondered idly where they were walking to until Nicole appeared, walking with a boy Darren didn't recognise. They approached the dwindling group and separated, saying nothing.

Another two or three times, the teenagers paired off. It clicked and he understood, now, what he had to do. Look at Nicole, say the words. Ask the question.

Do you want to go for a walk?

His blood pounded in his head.

What was worse, Nicole seemed to be waiting for it. She lingered close to him, not engaging much with anyone else. But no matter how close they were, the words shied far from his throat.

Eventually, the English boy who went for a walk with the pudgy girl came back alone. He circled around for five minutes before approaching Nicole.

'Do you want to go for a walk?'

Nicole glanced at Darren.

'Ok,' she shrugged.

As they turned out of sight Nicole's mum shouted down from her balcony, 'Emma! Where's Nicole?'

Emma shouted back that she was just away for a walk.

'Ah Christ is that – come up here now!' her mum pointed at a boy: '*you*, what's your name?'

The boy scurried off.

Half an hour later Nicole and the English boy returned. Darren, two giggling boys and a grumpy girl were all that were left by the pool. The English boy sauntered off, satisfied with his night's work.

For a while no-one spoke.

Nicole sighed. 'So,' she spoke to Darren; 'do you want to go for a walk?'

The few left looked at him.

Darren nodded. 'Yes please.'

Nicole led him around the back of the complex, overlooking a sea of black rock. Three male workers walked toward them, checking things were closed and locked. They noticed Darren and split off the path, their cold eyes casting over him as he passed.

'Do you know them?' Nicole asked.

'No,' he said, and shivered.

The last orange streaks were leaving the sky and taking with it the blue of the day. Darren and Nicole sat shoulder to shoulder at the top of a set of concrete steps.

'Those crickets are so loud,' she said.

'I think they're called cicadas,' he said.

'So, do you want to kiss me or...?'

'Yes.'

He followed her lead and they kissed open mouthed, slow and repetitive, like timid pink kissing fish. Almost immediately, an urge to touch her breast boiled within him. Either one. It wasn't important which, or to touch both. His hand moved from her thigh up. His heart beat like running flip-flops.

Nicole pulled away.

Emma wheezed between her knees. 'Mum, wants you, to come, in. Right now. Seriously, she's pissed.'

Nicole huffed and sprung to her feet. 'Fine,' she said, and to Darren, 'what took you so long?'

'…. If I told you I was dropped as a child–'

Their lovely-lilted laughter faded with their footslaps, and Darren was left with whatever it was making noise out in the night.

Cultural Appropriation

Emily S. Cooper

After Paul Muldoon

I am a shy beast in this language.
Split from my laissez faire vowels,
I lose the native lustre of my throat.

In one tongue I am a goddess,
languid as the locks on Helen's head.
In another I am a knotted rope.

I lie among these words as in
a strange bed. An unheated room
in a cracked-out love-hotel.

One hand on my breast, one flicking
through my notes. I think of all
the family words I've carried in this world.

Gollygaleen, tape leisure, glubbs.
It's all the proof I need, to be misunderstood.

Marseille

Emily S. Cooper

He had created a type of 3D paint,
was one of the first things he told us.

As we followed him upstairs to his plant-
filled apartment, we decided he was lying.

It wasn't long until he told us about Mexico;
kidnapped by cartels, held hostage for weeks,

his father and grandfather were mercenaries
in the French Foreign Legion.

He introduced us to his three-passport dog,
four French girls and his pal from Belgium.

Every day there were new visitors.
The Belgian was the last man in the house.

When we woke up to find him tucking us in,
we realised he didn't actually sleep.

Each night he tried to persuade
a new girl into his bed:

the Germans were more easily led,
the French a severe *non*.

He spoke French with an American accent,
had the physique of a young Adonis

and described to us in detail
how he used to build bombs.

We were taught about an old style of torture
while we sat in a drained fountain,

among the graffiti we learned that if
you swallow a button, and pull it back up,

your body evacuates everything south
and north.

Six months later he called me
in the middle of the night.

I didn't pick up, but remembered the paintings
he showed us before we left,

the faces lighting up, leaping out.

Lough Derg

Emily S. Cooper

On a hydrofoil out
to an island of pilgrims
on an undercover mission
that so far hasn't made an appearance

to an island of pilgrims
all dressed up for a saviour
who so far hasn't made an appearance
on one of the pieces of dry toast

all dressed up for a saviour,
arranged like the wings of a swan fed
on one of the pieces of dry toast.
The young girls are sleeping

arranged like the wings of a swan, fed
up with all of the walking and praying.
The young girls are sleeping
in the pews and I am standing

up with all of the walking and praying
pilgrims thinking of the Lord.
In the pews, I am standing
out amongst the believers;

pilgrims thinking of our Lord
on an undercover mission
out amongst the believers
on a hydrofoil of love.

SEX

Emily S. Cooper

A clandestine glance through
the sash window is enough
to satisfy my suspicions
about their crockery cupboard.
Yes, it is full to the top with
cups, saucers and plates. Collected
and purchased with an eye so keen
and discerning that even stacked
unevenly they seem
kerned to a magnification of 10.
I imagine their cutlery drawer
and its handsome shrapnel
of stainless steel and vintage silver.
I bet they have at least one
copper pot, and a steel enamel saucepan
for hot chocolate. I'm not jealous.

Looking for the Big House

Emily S. Cooper

Having reversed back up two drives
flanked by parish dogs
doing their duty by barking and nipping
at the wheels of my father's car
(gone mouldy inside and with one door
that only closes when you slam it
just right) we decided we had been searching
along the wrong side of the road.

We followed a loop that passed
both the field my mother said
she'd leave to one of us,
and the beach we sat on as children,
now manned by rows of mussel cages;
an industry for the profit
of only one man.

The shore-front of my ancestral town
had long died when the factories
moved out, leaving brown buildings
overshadowing a once attractive promenade.
Those who complained received brown letters
in the post, and not the bribing kind.

The Big House was on sale
for a pittance, with fire damage.
A neighbour told us that half the country
had been down to look at its
five bedroom glory, with a sea view.

As we turned down towards the roof-scape
a woman emerged from her bungalow,
spray-paint can in hand,
to colour her creeping juniper gold.

The Great Escape*

Emily S. Cooper

Doherty's emergence from the ladies'
did not shock the locals in their seats.
They did not really notice the dirt
up his arms or on his cheek.

They had better things to think about:
darts, football, politics.
The newest member of the council;
whose wake it was this week.

Doherty's wife sat at home alone,
watching Coronation Street.

He'd gone to bed early again,
lifted up Rita Hayworth and his spoon.
Dug for Ireland, for Liberty,
for drinking Guinness and playing pool.

* *'Omagh's 'Shawshank Husband' Dug Tunnel From Bedroom To Pub Over 15 Years'* –
Tyrone Tribulations, 25th September 2014.

The Exile

Andrew Maguire

In Zurich, it was just after dinner, and while he was getting ready to leave for the library she was at the sink, and a silence, festering over weeks and months in a room that was originally considered good-enough-for-the-time-being, was hanging heavy in the air.

Bronsky burst in, hurried and excited. She dropped a glass and it rang loud, cracking against the porcelain sink, and their guest paused. From the table, he glared towards her and back to Bronsky, who offered no apology, no acknowledgement of the broken glass, lying in pieces in the murky water. She put her hand in after it and almost instantly let out a small cry and withdrew it sharply, as if bitten.

'It's happened. It has finally happened,' Bronsky declared, throwing the evening newspaper across the table.

He felt her eyes over his shoulder as he read the headline. It was true. Hundreds of miles away, in Petrograd, their revolution had begun. She leaned over him and pulled the paper forward, and he watched as the red blood trickled from her finger.

When something significant happens, is it not supposed to happen quickly? He knew things were happening that way in Petrograd, but in Zurich, though he tried to act quickly, those around him could not keep up. The question had not been whether or not to return to Russia, but how to do it and how soon it could be done; no matter how many plans were proposed, nothing was successfully arranged. He waited in a world of perpetual imminence.

At last, after negotiations with Germany, they obtained the necessary documents for travel. He knew this was no favour from the Germans. It was an invitation to return to Russia and cause the inevitable trouble that would distract Russia from the war. But such things were mere politics, and no concern of his, so finally, here they were, all thirty-two of them, in a single, sealed carriage: A runaway Russian embassy, cutting through war-stricken Europe, en route to war-stricken Russia. As the train sets off with a jolt from Gottmadingen, Germany, on the edge of the Swiss border, Lenin feels a lurch in his stomach, and it all seems painfully slow, as he is forced to wait, wait until he can take control.

'This has been a long time coming,' says Grigory Zinoviev, sitting across from him in the carriage cabin, cut off from the rest of the travellers.

'I suppose you're referring to the train?'

'Well.'

'Arranging transportation was not easy, no.'

'Do you fear what you will see? Do you fear what the war has done?'

'No. If war is what was needed to get us to this point, then we must accept her other consequences as well.'

'It has been a sort of turning point,' Zinoviev says.

His eyes pull away from the window and Zinoviev feels his cold stare. 'No, it is not a turning point. There have been none, and there will be no turning points. It has all built towards this, has always been building to what will come.'

His gaze returns to the landscape that flows past the window. He believes it to be so. Although things speed up and slow down – it is so slow! he thinks, as he looks out the window and takes in each passing field in detail – the direction never changes. He can feel the train, as slow as it is, travelling towards Petrograd like a bullet travelling through history. Things will get faster when we arrive in Petrograd, he assures himself. If they don't arrest me when we get there.

He stares down at the sheets of paper on the table, but takes nothing in because he can feel her presence on the other side of the cabin door. He looks up at Zinoviev who has pen and paper in hand and has been transcribing everything he has said.

'She knows not to disturb me,' he says. 'So she stands out there and waits until there is no option but for me to invite her in, and thinks that this doesn't count.' He looks at the notes Zinoviev has been writing. 'Did you get everything?'

'Yes.'

'Good,' he says, and sits back.

'Your wife sir,' Zinoviev says.

'Never mind that,' Lenin says, and he raises his hand towards the window of the carriage door. He closes his eyes. A moment.

He is a student of revolution, but he has never witnessed an entire revolutionary movement before, and it angers him somewhat that he will not witness one now. His exile in Switzerland has meant that no matter how big a part he is about to play, he has missed the beginning. His frustration is balanced with a sense of opportunism: he is relieved to be seeing the revolution at all. It is not unexpected that it has happened within his generation's lifetime, but still, he is relieved to have lived long enough. When did I last see the physician? he wonders. One week ago. All had been fine, but it will be a while before I see one again.

What his absence to this point has meant, he is not sure. He sits on the train like a man going to visit a loved one in hospital. He has heard reports on how she is doing, opinions on how she looks, but when he sets his eyes on her, he knows his heart will feel differently than in any scenario he has been able to imagine thus far.

He opens his eyes. Zinoviev is nodding to the door again. Lenin sighs. 'Come in!' he shouts.

He sees his brother Alexander standing with a bag over his head. His two feet rest on the floor boards for the usual two seconds, then for the thousandth time the floor gives way. His brother falls, his neck snaps, his feet dangle, he is dead in an instant and with him dies every idea in his head and every want in his heart. All his potential influence vanishes. Foolish, Lenin thinks. A careless waste.

He lowers the book in the otherwise empty carriage. The sound of voices singing in enthusiastic unison echoes throughout the train.

Arise, awaken, working people!
Arise against the enemy, hungry folk!
Ring out, cry of the people's vengeance!
Forward! Forward! Forward! Forward! Forward!

Where is Zinoviev?

'Zinoviev?' he shouts. 'Zinoviev?'

A few seconds pass and Zinoviev appears at the door.

'Yes?'

'Make that singing stop, can't you?'

'I will ask, but.'

'But what?'

'They are already complaining about the condition of the toilet, if I tell them…'

'What is wrong with the toilet?'

'You have said that anyone smoking must do so there.'

'So that they don't bother the rest of us, yes.'

'Well, it is not always available for its primary use now.'

'Well they can smoke or they can…Just make the noise stop, will you?'

'I will try,' Zinoviev says as he closes the door.

What did songs ever do? he wonders. Distracted, he puts the book down, looks out the window and listens to the gentle, rhythmic beat of the train along the tracks.

For-ward! For-ward! For-ward! For-ward! For-ward!

He sits with his eyes closed and the table of stale bread, hard cheese and bad wine in front of him. It is not her fault, but she is sitting across from him and he has nothing to say and wishes that she would leave. He opens his eyelids wide enough for light to come in, then wider, and she comes into focus before him.

'Aren't you hungry?' she asks.

'No.'

'They don't complain about the food out there,' she says, and nods to the door, and to the people beyond it.

'Yes, well that's the problem, isn't it?'

With her sitting there, the dirty, tarnished seat of the coach looks filthier than ever. Her inexpensive but well cared for clothes shame all that is around her.

'Have you nothing to say to me anymore?' she asks.

'It is not you, Nadezhda. It is that the time for speaking has stopped.'

'Even speaking to me?'

'I said it's not about you.'

'If you're only treating me like everyone else then it is about me.'

Days and nights pass. He lies awake while she sleeps. At the stop at Frankfurt station he listens to shouting, as two loud German voices address the others on-board. The shouting doesn't last long, and the lack of audible response means he does not intervene. He assumes they are reacting to the singing of songs of revolution. He has no objection to their orders that it stop. Another station. A more significant stop this time. Twenty hours at Potsdam Station in Berlin. She doesn't always sleep beside him anymore. Then the ferry to Sweden. The meetings with Swedish communists and the Mayor of Stockholm are tedious. It feels slower than ever. Eventually they set off again through Sweden and towards Finland, in the direction of Petrograd. He knows the world around him is moving fast. No doubt questions are being asked. Letters will be travelling around Europe, through Germany, Britain, France and Russia, asking questions, moving faster than they are. Will they make it to Petrograd? What will happen when they do? Will Russia remain in the war? The same thoughts travel through Lenin head.

It was science and University that took his older brother to Petrograd. Lenin admired him for his academic success, then he found a collection of books in his room which were full of ideas and theories, and discovered that his brother had a political side. Soon after, and as though all at once, his brother was arrested, charged with conspiring to assassinate the Tsar, and executed; taken from his family in the same year that God had taken their father. A spark was lit within Lenin and he followed his brother's footsteps, leaving God behind and going to the same university, where he sat in the same libraries, read the same books at the same tables and felt that same universal pull of youth that says go, go now, and change the world. But he hadn't. His brother had acted, and had died. A spark was there, but sparks are easily extinguished.

'What are you reading?' Zinoviev asks.

Lenin lowers the book and looks across at him.

'You haven't read this?'

'No. What is it?'

'Chernyshevsky.'

Zinoviev looks back blankly and Lenin, frustrated, explains. 'What Is To Be Done? by Nikolai Chernyshevsky.'

'Oh.'

'You've heard of it?'

'Yes.'

'As you should have.'

'You've read it before?'

'I first read it in University,' he explains, holding up the worn out copy of the book. 'I read it after I read Marx, while those around me were reading Marx again.'

'I don't know it.'

'I read it again in Siberia. You know what I like about it? It has ideas of revolution, which you will have read elsewhere. But it is a novel, so the characters actually carry it through.'

'Easy in a novel,' Zinoviev says.

'Whereas in life it is easier to just talk, to work in theories. Some people expect too much of an idea. They expect it to act itself out.'

'But theories can be developed.'

'This is not a conversation, Zinoviev, that I will have again.'

'But.'

'You frustrate me. Go. Go overlook the carriage or something.'

'Pardon?'

'Get out. Leave me be. Or better yet, find someone else, someone that will not bore me with the same old questions,' Lenin says, and Zinoviev gets up and closes the door behind him.

'It is death that angers them.' Kolosov says, as he sits across from Lenin, with a chess board on the table between them. 'It is why the Tsar is gone. He became Commander in Chief of the armed forces, and all blood spilled on the front line was on his hands. And his absence too. He left our country in the hands of Rasputin and Alexandra, and they…'

'Rumour,' Lenin interrupts.

'Regardless, the people want an end to the war.'

'Of course they do,' Lenin says, studying the board.

'And the provisional government isn't giving it to them,' Kolosov says.

'Who says this?'

'My wife.'

'By letter?'

'Yes.'

'Is that who you are returning to?'

'Yes,' he says, and seems to look at Nadezhda as he speaks. 'To my wife and children.'

'Your wife is right. The provisional government will never provide peace.'

'Too many Russians are dying.'

'That's true,' Lenin says, and there is a silence, before Nadezhda speaks.

'Death is not always the worst part of war,' she says.

'No?' Kolosov asks.

Lenin is silent. 'Think of your father,' she says, turning to him. 'Your family were hunters, Lenin. You hunted yourself, around your home, on your land. And you have said before how one day, as you did so, your father explained to you what he thought was the essence of hunting.

'He said there was a man that fished a lake his whole life. The lake was on the grounds of a rich family, the Rudnikovs, and was surrounded by woods. In the man's youth, while he was out on the lake, he would shiver at the sound of the gun shots around him as Rudnikov shot the birds from the trees. But even while the gunshots sounded, the sound of the birds singing continued. Then one day, in his old age, the man was out on the lake again, with a friend. Do you hear that? the man asked. What is it? the friend replied. It is the birds singing. Rudnikov is dead, but the birds remain, and we can hear them sing.'

They are silent, he feels her hand in his, unaware which of them made the movement, and he remembers why he is here. He looks to Kolosov, who looks back at him, and also remembers why he is preferring his company to Zinoviev's. The time for his ideas to be questioned is over.

'Checkmate,' Lenin says.

Kolosov looks at the board, mildly confused for a second, before seeing his mistake and accepting defeat.

'Will you do me a favour comrade, and write down what I dictate to you?' Lenin asks.

'Of course.'

The train is slowing down, and Lenin pushes the chessboard away.

'Let me read you something, comrade', he says, and lifts the book.

'But does it really help if a person doesn't realize what he lacks, or, if he does, he insists that he doesn't need it at all? That's an illusion, a fantasy. Human nature is stifled by reason, circumstances, and pride. It keeps silent and doesn't make itself known to one's consciousness, all the while silently doing its work of understanding life.'

'What do they lack?'

'What have I been dictating to you? What is it that you have written down?'

'Peace, bread, land,' Kolosov says.

'Peace, bread, land,' Lenin repeats.

His wife opens the carriage door and enters.

'What is it?' he asks.

'We're stopping at the Russian frontier. There's a crowd.'

'What do you mean a crowd?'

'From the front of the carriage they can see a crowd at the train station ahead.'

Kamenev and Stalin are here, ready to greet him. It hasn't been expected, but he stands on the platform, just outside the doors of the train, and the words come naturally. Amongst the near carnival atmosphere, with the train about to set off, he ends the speech quickly and with a question.

'Are they going to arrest us when we get to Petrograd?'

The crowd in front of him laugh, and the sound echoes behind them as the train leaves the platform.

'There is your answer,' Zinoviev says, inside the train.

'And to think,' Nadezhda says, 'I was worried that we'd struggle to get a carriage in Petrograd to take us to our lodgings.'

'We're safe, then. No danger of arrest?' Zinoviev asks.

'I don't know,' Lenin says. 'But after that reaction to my question, one thing is for sure; whether it is those who laughed, or me for having asked, someone is going to look foolish.'

The final leg of the journey, like the rest before it, is slow. But he feels a rush as it gets closer. It has built to this. 'It is not because my ideas are special, my friend,' he says to Kolosov, as he moves another pawn on the chess board. 'I have taken such care, simply because I know I am the one that will put these ideas into action. Now is the time.'

The stops are more frequent than ever now, and they are gaining passengers. The stations are lined with people, and several Russian soldiers board the train at each stop. Soon it is near packed tight. But no matter. It is getting faster. He can feel it. A fire is burning in him, one that will not be easy put out. He looks out the window and the crowds are bigger at nearly every station they pass. One of the soldiers leans out the window as they pass a station and shouts.

'Long live the world revolution!'

Soon they are there. The train comes to a final halt in Petrograd. He is on his feet. The carriage is full of people, but the path is cleared for them as they make their way to the exit. They step out onto the platform, setting foot on Russian ground again. There is a crowd. They cheer. He raises one hand and reaches for her with the other as they stride confidentially forward. He hears them sing. It is time.

The Air Marshal

Joseph Robinson

John Erikson hated coach. It was the smell. He'd gone to the toilets only ten minutes prior and had regretted the decision since he stepped back into the cabin. The musk of stale fatigue: of those who'd not showered since they began their trip. It would cling to his three-piece suit, he knew. He hated it, and he hated them. He hated himself for being there.

The cabin shook, and he forgot the smell entirely. Luggage on either side of him rumbled with every jerk and jolt. He feared a seam-strained suitcase would burst from its compartment and crush him.

Seatbelt signs pinged around him. Seats and passengers merged together, mere shadows left and right. The way forward, dim. Lit by aisle lights at his feet, and the glow of seatbelt signs above him. His vision tunnelcd: focused on the aisle. The only path he had.

As above, so below, he thought. *Wait… what's that——*

Before he could track his thought the aisle dropped beneath him. What was firm and grounding, gone.

~

John woke to the digital rattle of the hotel phone. His head throbbed. With every chime, pressure spread to his temples. The pain of it, a crown bolted in place. He was thankful it wasn't an older phone. A hard, rotary-ring would have been unbearable.

He reached for it, eyes shut, and knocked his near-empty Jameson bottle from the nightstand.

'I'm awake,' he said and hung up.

He rolled onto his back, pinching the bridge of his nose and waited for the throb to end. When it didn't, he pulled his phone from beneath the pillow. No messages. Just the time and date above the face of a beautiful girl on his lock-screen. Auburn hair fell in soft curls to her shoulders, her eyes bright green.

He clicked the sleep button: the phone gave its shutter sound and darkened. He tossed it aside and sat at the edge of his bed. His toes grazed the Jameson and he rolled it beneath his foot a moment.

Fuck it.

He grabbed the bottle and finished the rest.

John crossed to the window and dried his hair. He felt better after the shower: the pain in his head felt less bolted, more lightly screwed.

He opened the curtains. A sliver of pink stretched across the horizon, but he could not see the sun. Fifty yards away, stood the hotel's sign. White script stretched across a wide blue block:

America's Best Value Inn

He gave his hair a quick tousle, then collected his clothes from the floor and stuffed them into his carryon. He checked his satchel, to ensure his things were there: money-clip, cardholder, passport, Neil Gaiman's *American Gods*, MacBook, earbuds, pen, notebook, badge. He placed the bags by the door, then took the garment-bag from the closet and dressed himself in the three-piece suit it held.

Before he left, he opened the nightstand drawer and retrieved the holstered SIG Sauer he placed there the night before. He drew the gun, slid the magazine from the grip and cleared the chamber. Nothing spat out. He replaced the magazine, checked the safety, and holstered his weapon. He secured the holster to his belt: at his back, beneath his vest and jacket. Dressed and ready, he grabbed his phone. No messages.

John waited on the curb outside Newark Liberty for the cabby to bring his bags. He didn't offer to help, or grab them himself, for the same reason he chose not to take the bus: cover. A wealthy marketing executive, on his way to London, wouldn't. He looked the part and kept a few business cards in his wallet for the more inquisitive.

He thumbed through Flipboard while the cabby placed his bags at his feet. He gave the cabby the 'one-minute' gesture with his other hand. Without a word, or looking, he reached into his jacket and retrieved his money clip and handed the cabby two twenties. He took his bags from the curb and walked into the terminal. The trick, he'd observed, was to not acknowledge the help — or the cash he handed out.

John bought himself a dirty-chai latte and sat in the corner of the airport cafe — back to the wall, to watch the crowds. In college, the dirty-chai provided the kickstart needed to work. He hoped it would again. Instead, he watched the cursor blink for ten minutes. For the next forty minutes, he nursed his latte and browsed Facebook and Reddit: scrolling, clicking, reading nothing. Bored, he opened his photo albums and sifted through his time in Glasgow.

He'd gotten his degrees there. At the time, the difference between US tuition and the UK's International Student tuition was nominal, and he had to live on loans anyway — the extra thousand per year, a mere leaf on the tree. Looking at the pictures, he didn't regret the choice.

Trips to the highlands. Edinburgh scenery. The Giant's Causeway and the Mourne Mountains from his summer in Northern Ireland. Despite his job, it was the only time he felt like he truly travelled.

His companions changed often. Most only pub-pals. Toward the end, his companions dwindled to one: the girl with auburn hair and green eyes.

John checked his email for his briefing: inspect and guard was all he got from it. Before he went to work, he checked his account balances. Just enough to make this month's loan payments. Just.

He checked his phone before clearing security. Nothing.

The plane cleared his inspection. Most did. The only exciting thing John had done since he started the job was escort a drunk from the plane before it took off. Overall, the job was babysitting: sit and watch the cabin door. A waste of tax-payer money, he thought. He didn't feel bad about it. If the tax-payers didn't want to help pay for his college, he figured they could pay his loans. First-class flights, too — of course.

The Virgin Clubhouse felt wide and open: filled with booths, cushioned armchairs and small drink-tables. Lit by chandeliers and recessed fixtures along the wall. The decor angled and sharp. Round chairs and plump cushions softened the edges. To John, the vibe welcomed and cautioned at once.

Except for the bartender and a man seated in a cushioned armchair, John was alone. There was another hour before the flight boarded. The other firstclassers wouldn't arrive for another forty minutes. He sat the end of the bar to face the entrance.

'What can I get you?' asked the bartender.

John eyed the entrance and hesitated.

Fuck it.

'Whiskey. No ice. Would you wipe the counter,' he told the bartender.

Another trick he'd learned. Command, never request. Always add 'would you.' Soften the edge.

John had his laptop out when the bartender brought his whiskey. He plugged in his earbuds and played *Songs from a Ghost Town.* He hoped it would help his focus.

He sipped his whiskey and watched the Clubhouse entrance between the cursor's blinks. As 'When I Come Back Again,' began, the first passenger entered. A leather briefcase hung across his trim, suited chest.

His skin a burnt-sand color: beard thick, but groomed. He wore a grey suit with a cobalt shirt. His turban the same grey shade as his tie.

~

This ain't turbulence, he thought.

John pulled himself up by the armrests of 52C and 52D. To his left, lightning forked outside an open window.

Something's wrong.

He used seats and passengers alike to steady himself. When he reached first-class, he dropped into his seat. The turbaned man, across the aisle, looked horrified.

~

John watched the turbaned man seat himself at a booth angled toward the bar. The man caught his eye and gave John a smile and nod. John returned it.

The bartender took the man's order. John went back to his whiskey and empty document.

Probably not even Muslim. Sikh, maybe?

John lived near a mosque in Glasgow and passed it two, three times daily. He couldn't recall ever seeing a turban. Kufis and thobes, but not turbans. Most, though, dressed like any other casual city-dweller. Often, when their service ended, they stood outside and talked while the children ran and played. John, while not a religious man, enjoyed walking past them. It reminded him of Sacred Heart, the church his grandparents attended when he was young. There, too, adults gathered and talked while he and other children played tag in the parking lot.

He checked his phone. Nothing. He ordered another whiskey.

John reread the hundred words he managed. It was slow, hookless. He rested his head in his hands and sipped his drink: the liquor, at last, wrapped his head in a warm haze. He deleted his paragraph.

Write drunk, he mused and took another gulp.

When he sat up and put his hands on the keyboard, he couldn't see. Thin fingers pressed against his eyes and he could smell a faint, fruity perfume.

'Guess who?' the voice as sweet as the perfume he smelled.

Before John could guess, the hands fell from his face and a woman sat beside him. Brown hair curled at her shoulders and her blue eyes where bright and playful. She wore a red flight attendant's blazer and black skirt. It complimented her copper skin.

'Hey…' John began. He eyed the breast of her jacket, and hoped her name-tag would be there. It wasn't.

'Lacey,' she said. Her smile was gentle, flirty.

'Of course. Sorry…'

John had flown several flights with her, but they had never conversed beyond a passing greeting.

'You don't remember much from last night do you?' she asked.

He shook his head. He remembered drinking at Mugs Pub. That she had been there, and they spoke briefly — a passing hello, he thought — but little else.

'That's okay.' Her smile faded as she turned toward the bar. She waved the bartender down from the other end of the bar.

'Shouldn't you be preparing for the flight?' John asked.

'Shouldn't you?' She winked. 'Relax. I just need coffee. Still a tad hungover.'

Lacey gave her order and waited at the bar. She crossed her legs and swiveled in the barstool. She kept her shoulders forward, but her hips toward John.

His cheeks flushed, and he couldn't tell if it was the whiskey or Lacey. He kept it discreet, quick peeks from his screen. but he couldn't help but look at her. The cross of her legs left a small gap in her skirt. Nothing to get excited over, but he peeked when he could.

I wonder if she knows what she's doing…

'What are you working on?' Lacey asked.

'Oh… nothing.' John blushed, and he was certain she noticed. 'Just a story, I guess.'

She leaned over and looked at his screen.

'I could be wrong,' she smiled. 'But don't writers write?'

He closed his laptop. He hated being reminded that he squandered the reason he took this job: the ample time to write.

'Wait… how'd—'

'I remember more of last night than you do.' She winked, and John wondered if it was a nervous tic or if there's a joke he wasn't getting.

He checked his phone.

'So that's what she looks like,' Lacey said. 'Pretty.'

'How—'

'Please. When you weren't talking about writing or Nigel Gaiman, you rambled on about your time in Glasgow and…' she pointed to his phone. '…her.'

'Sorry,' John said and put his phone in his pocket. 'That couldn't have been fun for you.'

'It's fine. Honest.'

The bartender brought the coffee and Lacey thanked him.

'Just wish you remembered more of our discussion,' she continued.

'Like what?'

'Well, how — in this line of work — open-relationships are the only way to go.'

John felt a catch in his throat.

'Relax,' she said. 'You weren't into it,' she laughed.

She blew on her coffee before taking a sip, smiling at him as she did.

She must know what she's doing. She enjoys this.

'So does that mean…'

She giggled, and John wasn't sure if it was flirtation or contempt.

'I've got to go,' she said. 'But maybe this will help you remember: get it on the rocks.'

She began to leave. Before she took two steps, she snapped her fingers and spun on her heel. Her eyes on her feet. She put her hand on his shoulder and leaned close to his ear.

'By the way. Start keeping your badge in your room when you're off-duty, Marshal Erikson.'

He stared after her and watched as she walked away. His mind raced as he tried to recall the night before. His phone chimed and interrupted his thoughts. He took it from his jacket. There, at the top, he read her message without tapping it. Four words was all he got. He put his phone away and waved to the bartender.

He tossed another whiskey back in a single swallow.

The turbaned man sat across from John and spent much of the flight on a laptop, typing away at whatever he was working on. John spent most of his time watching Lacey work the bar. Casually, he'd mask it with a stretch and quick look around the cabin. He'd grabbed *American Gods* from his satchel, more as added subtlety than to read. When he wasn't watching Lacey, he tried again to remember his night with her.

He remembered they shared a love for 'How I Met Your Mother,' and she laughed when he said that was one reason he chose his job: he enjoyed the pun. He remembered sharing more than he should have about the distance between himself and his partner. That he'd taken this flight to surprise her in London and planned to walk into HarperCollins with a bouquet of white lilies — her favorite — convinced it would fix everything. He remembered nothing about the rocks.

Fuck it.

He went the bar.

'Good evening, sir. How can I help you?' Lacey asked.

'Whiskey,' he ordered. 'On the rocks.'

Lacey smiled.

'Right away.'

She turned around, scooped ice into a glass and poured Bushmill's over it. He grimaced. Lacey took a pen from her apron and scribbled a note on a napkin: and slide them both to him.

Lacey took off her apron and walked down the left aisle. John took his whiskey and read the note: **Take the right aisle. All the way back. Wait 5. First on the left. Knock once, then twice**.

As John walked down the aisle, more of the night came back to him. He waded through the stench of coach. The stale exhaustion and sweat jarred like smelling salts. It helped. When he reached the rear of the plane he knew. He stopped and swayed outside the door.

Fuck it, he thought.

He knocked as Lacey instructed. He'd never see her again anyway.

~

The plane shook and luggage rumbled in the overhead compartments. Panicked screams, short lived, filled the plane with every jolt forward and every altitude drop. John tightened his seatbelt, half-convinced the plane would split in two.

We're fine, he told himself. *They're built for this. We're fine. Worry when the masks fall. Focus on something else.*

John closed his eyes, took a deep breath, and for the first time noticed the smell of first-class. It smelled clean. Like generic laundry soap meant to trigger thoughts of summer, or rain, but didn't. He took another, deeper breath and wished he could smell the Highlands again. The smell of rain, real rain, or the Atlantic spray on the Giant's Causeway. Her.

It hit him then: his hate and love for her, and for himself. His hatred of the strain between them, and how they fizzled to nothing. His whiskey stupors, and failed writing and the wasted degree in it. He hated Lacey and the turbaned man across from him. The coach passengers and every gussied-up first-classer around him. As the plane shook and dropped and rolled: he realized it didn't matter. None of it.

The cabin lights flickered, and John took his phone from his pocket. He opened messenger and began to type. Not a response, just a message. He sent it, then looked up. The turbaned man held a white-knuckled grip on his arm rests: eyes closed tight, his lips moving silently.

'Hey! Dude!' John called.

The turbaned man opened his eyes and John waved.

'I gotta know. Sikh or Muslim?'

The turbaned man's faced twisted, and John couldn't tell if it was horror or confusion. He reached into a pocket and took his badge from it. He held it open to the turbaned man. The lights dimmed.

'Doesn't matter, but I gotta know. Sikh or Muslim?'

'M-Muslim…'

John hung his head and laughed. At himself mostly, and the absurdity of it all. When he looked up, the turbaned man looked angry and hurt. He didn't have to say it. John knew what he was thinking.

'I'm sorry,' John said. 'I was just trying to pay my student loans.'

The plane dropped and rocked and the masks fell from above. John laughed. He thought of *Fight Club — oxygen gets you high.*

He reread her message: **We should break up.**

He reread his. The blue checkmark beside it more maddening than everything else.

Fuck it, he thought and slipped his mask on. He breathed deep and long.

We're all going down anyway. Coach, pilot, everyone in between. None of it matters.

He glanced at his phone, one last time. He watched the blue checkmark change to her picture. The same as his lock screen. Her face beside his message: **I love you.**

He smiled and began to sing to himself. His favorite verse from Trampled by Turtles.

'When I come back, lord, when I come back again.'

The cabin trembled and rattled.

'Annie take me back to my home.'

An overhead compartment opened, luggage fell into the aisle.

'Annie take me back to my home, my home.'

The lights flickered off and never came back on.

'Ain't gonna roam no more.'

Fatback

James Patterson

Martin was finishing a fuel-siphon from a forty-two-gallon barrel of oil with a screwdriver, a mallet, a funnel, a cork and tin bucket—something taught to him by Mags on his first day—before pouring its contents into the boiler at the far end of the foil-lined bunker.

Alaska turned out to be much colder than he would have anticipated, and it was a mistake to have left the fuel so close to the door where the air could get in and freeze anything that wasn't well covered over. A mistake he wouldn't be making again.

Once he was finished, he made sure that the tassels on his gloves were well pulled, the thermal-scarf stretched tight above the tip of his nose and snow goggles securely fastened on his head, before venturing out into the freezing white and trudging back along the twine that led the way to his bunk.

Winter on North Shore normally meant visibility of no more than a few feet. Mags told him that several of her predecessors had been lax about taking such precautions and had either lost body parts to frostbite or worse, had wandered off into the white never to be seen again. It was this that scared Martin more than anything during his first few months at the outpost, and now he didn't take any chances. He didn't consider himself completely safe until he saw the caribou antlers mounted above the door of his living quarters—even when the weather was clear—and further still until he was sat in front of the stove drinking coffee from Mags's *So Fucking What?* Metallica mug.

Once he got safely installed Martin usually hung his wet clothes up and changed into his sweats. Blizzard conditions were meant to last for another couple of days, and in the meantime there was nothing more to be done, but he had enough fuel to see him through the rest of the month and enough food in the cabin that he didn't have to step outside again for most of that time. He just wished that the weather would let up a little so he could check his *Facebook* account and maybe put in a radio call to Mags. It was his niece's fifth birthday back home and he wanted to leave her a message, or at least look at some of the photos his sister, Allie, had put up on her page.

Life at the outpost was tranquil much of the time and was an opportunity he was grateful to Mags for having gave him, but it was also cripplingly lonely and unforgiving if one was unprepared to truly commit .

Days like these were particularly long and tedious. Even in good weather the landscape on North Shore was nothing but ice and rock for miles around, with the occasional sprig of hard grass or willow bark— which Mags said could be made into a tea that promoted sleep.

Fairbanks had been much more to his liking; anonymous but just civilized enough that he could forget himself in a warm wood-panelled bar with a TV and jukebox, and maybe a good-time girl who wanted to know what things were like elsewhere. It was much easier to forget in that sort of environment.

On North Shore however, even the frontier idea of Alaska was betrayed by the constant snow. There was no game-hunting or log-chopping or trading ice-fish for whale blubber; not even domesticated husky dogs were suited to this kind of weather. You couldn't do anymore than just sit inside the cabin drinking coffee, playing with the comms radio, reading, watching movies or jacking off. Mags had told him it was mainly reading that kept her sane during her time there, and there was an almost full library of paperbacks stacked on a cinderblock shelf constructed near the window.

But Mags's taste was not to Martin's taste, and anything left behind simply seemed an aggravation of his loneliness—Dostoevsky, McCarthy, Baudelaire, *The Shining* by Stephen King. Martin wanted something that affirmed the natural goodness of life—finding nothing but horror and nihilism in the things he'd run away from—so films passed most of the time, among which *Frozen* and *Home Alone 2*—both of which reminded him of his niece—were his favourites.

Today though, he could not concentrate on film-watching. Before the storm he noticed a small, indistinct black shape circling the compound about a mile from the delivery runway, and he knew immediately that he was being tracked by a wolf or grizzly bear. This was the first such encounter he'd experienced, with Mags doing little to allay his fears when she finally arrived in her battered old bush-plane to deliver Martin's heating oil for Winter.

'Yeah,' she said pointing out to the middle-distance, squinting hard from the noontime glare of the snow. 'That'd likely be old Fatback. Son-of-a-bitch came through the wall of my cabin last time I was here, snapped my leg in half and took a bite outta my fuckin' neck. There was blood all over the place before I managed to get two rounds off in his back and he scampered off into the night with his tail between his legs. Probably got wise to my comin' back to visit you.'

'Is that why you left?' Martin asked.

'Among other things, yeah.' She patted the side of the plane when she said this. 'I suppose it just made me realise that I'm too fuckin' goddamn old to be fightin' Mother Nature in the Middle-of-Goddamn-Nowhere... I mean shit, Marty, I've got *grandkids*, and I wanna be alive to see at least one of 'em graduate college, y'know?'

'I guess,' Martin said.

That was three days ago, and every night since he'd spent sleeping with a cocked .44 Magnum—hung from the bedpost nearest his head—

in a leather holster given to him as a gift by his sister. Above the bed was a 45-70 bolt action Springfield rifle mounted just below the roof, with a box of ammunition kept in the top drawer of his bedside table. Indeed, Mags had warned him that the storm should not make him complacent about any potential predators. Bears and wolves were smart, she said, and would seek to draw their prey into open combat to be picked off; even if it took days. They were patient, she said, because there was nothing else to eat on North Shore. Nothing but foxes or the occasional hunter.

Still, as hard as life could be in Alaska, it didn't compare to the hardship Martin had already endured; nor were the sparse luxuries of the compound any different from the time he'd spent as an inhabitant of the *Tent City* back home.

He lived there for six months—after running away from home at 17—and built a wooden shanty using pallets stolen from a nearby railway yard, which he covered over at night with a blue tarpaulin. Electricity was rigged into the camp by an out-of-work electrician, using a series of stripped cables taken from the local boarded up houses and connecting them to a pylon through a network of cut-up garden hoses. He learned the art of survival quickly, scavenging for empty beer cans and tins of beans which he'd then cut in half, wash and use to boil stew or percolate coffee.

Life during the first summer months had been good, with one of the campers managing to procure a baby-grand to lead sing-alongs as the sun went down, and another who built a makeshift aviary for carrier pigeons.

It was the first and only time he'd felt part of a community, and sometimes he was even allowed to drink beer with the older campers, who viewed him through the prism of vulnerability and protected him from the outside world by accepting him as one of their own. Problems only arose later, when Allie—at 16—arrived with a 2 year old child in tow and nowhere else to stay.

Then winter kicked in, and suddenly Martin found himself in conflict with some other campers, who—like him—were competing for the portable gas burners and electric stoves used for heat in the evenings. Fist fights and stabbings became commonplace, and he learned quickly to be brutal and sometimes cold in order to keep his sister and niece safe from harm. Several good friends died from exposure, and it was not uncommon to step outside in the mornings to the crunch of snow and pipe-glass strewn on the ground from the night before.

It was this strength of character that Mags had recognised when she first passed the North Shore job to Martin. Already he'd converted the shell of an old schoolbus on the site—which had been half buried in snow and no-one was quite sure how to use—into a loading dock for the efficient and dry storage of wood for the stove. And that was after two years of wandering around Washington State and Vancouver, before finally coming north to Fairbanks and replying to Mags's ad in the local paper.

He also used the bus as a kind of watchtower; occasionally climbing onto its roof and looking out over the vast snowy plains in search of any incoming storm clouds or predators who might be on their way. And it was here he stood now, taking advantage of the passing calm afforded by the eye of the storm, to look out into the distance and see if he could spot old Fatback before nightfall came and the conditions were too dark or too unsettled to take a fair view.

'Nothing,' he said to himself, as he stepped down off the roof onto the snow-covered barrel he used as a step. 'Fucker's probably in hiding.'

Night had already started to fall over North Shore by the time he reached his cabin, and in the dying flat light, he noticed that the camp had suddenly taken on the ethereal royal blue richness of an underwater aquarium; likely attributable to the night-sky reflecting off the ground. Stars were nestled in a hole straight overhead—as North Shore passed through the eye of the storm—and Martin knew that he had to get inside quick, before the blizzards started again and he froze to death on the front step of his shack.

He hoped that where his niece and sister were was warm and that they were well-rested and safe and happy in their memories. Soon he'd be turning in, and unless he drank some willow bark to help him drop off to sleep, he knew he'd lie awake all night worrying about the bear coming through the door of the cabin and onto his bunk.

When he woke later he was dreaming of home, and imagining Allie and his niece under the same blanket—in front of the TV—the way they used to in his shack when they dropped off from exhaustion and knew they were protected and safely away from *Him*.

The blizzard had temporarily died down and the wind that howled between the barrels and storage containers was still, so that—when he heard the sound of rustling coming from outside the cabin door, by the corner of the front wall—the only explanation to Martin's mind was that old Fatback had finally wandered into camp to take him out and claim him as his meal.

Slowly, he sat up in bed and put the lamp on—being careful all the time not to make any sudden movements—before setting his laptop to one side, closing the screen and slipping into his high-top *Timberland* boots, which he wore over a pair of thermal long-johns and pyjama trousers. Next he grabbed his rifle and laid it on the bed, then fastened his sister's holster around his waist before checking the revolver to see if it was fully cocked and loaded. Last, he put on his overcoat and monkey-hat, then made for the door humming 'Let It Go' and praying silently that the noise he'd heard was an arctic fox, or maybe a wren who'd been blown off-course by the wind.

Nothing moved, but through the window—at the foot of the mound of snow banked against the side of the outhouse, which served as the compound's boiler room—Martin thought he could see the impressions of animal feet pressed into the ground. Visibility was poorer than it had been during the day, and as he opened the door and stepped out to take a look, feeling for the twine that guided his way between the outhouses of the compound, he discovered to his dismay that it had been severed; its frayed ends already starting to harden with frost when he picked up a strand and turned it over in his fingers.

Tentatively, he walked out into the night and approached the outhouse as best he could; making sure that what he'd really seen were the footprints of a bear and not just shadows created by a fevered, sleep-addled mind.

He went further, coming to the expected spot and finding nothing but white enveloping him from every side. There had been animal tracks, he was sure, though they were now covered over by snow and he was having great difficulty deciding what direction he should take to get back the way he came.

Chewing the Fat

Mick Draine

◄ **Cast of Characters** ►

FAT HEAD   Late thirties/early forties

NO NECK   Late thirties/early forties

RUSTY   Late fifties/early sixties

SPOOF   Twenties

Scene: Inside a kitchen of a restaurant in Belfast.

FAT HEAD enters, turns the lights on, turns the coffee machine on and exits. He returns with a book in his hand. He opens the book

FAT HEAD   Fuck! It's in the book.

NO NECK enters stage left

NO NECK   Is it in the book Fat Head?

FAT HEAD   It's in the book No Neck.

NO NECK   Pencil or pen?

FAT HEAD   Pen.

NO NECK   It's pen, it's in the book, it's true.

FAT HEAD   Looks like it. Pen, book, same name, table for three.

NO NECK   Three?

FAT HEAD   Three, but it will drop to 1 when he gets here, same as the other visits.

NO NECK   You're ready.

FAT HEAD   I know – but what's that got to do with it. Its Big Buller's name attached to this place. I'm fucked either way.

146

NO NECK   You're not fucked, you're ready, you know you
                 are. Be positive, Big Buller's fuck all, you're
                 the head chef and everyone knows it. Your
                 menu, your food, your way.

FAT HEAD   And if we get a star Big Buller's gets it. If we
                 don't, I don't. Can't win either way.

NO NECK   Can win. Can win every way. Your head chef,
                 everyone knows that.

FAT HEAD   I'm the sous chef, he is head chef and you're a
                 chef No Neck. On paper anyway.

NO NECK   Exactly, on paper, that's it. Everyone knows.
                 Besides I am the sous chef round here.

FAT HEAD   If you're the sous chef, that makes me head
                 chef and that doesn't work.

NO NECK   What?

FAT HEAD   We get on; no sous chef and head chef get on.
                 Coffee?

NO NECK   Cappuccino. Well we do get on what of it.

FAT HEAD   Wrong No Neck. Me as a sous chef and you
                 as a chef get on. Me as the head chef and you
                 as the sous chef would have to kill each other,
                 its tradition. It's the law and you know it.
                 Cappuccino?

NO NECK

Fuck the law. I'm the sous chef; you're the head chef, that's a fact. And yes cappuccino. I fancy one today. Head chef. Fact.

FAT HEAD

All head chefs are bastards, that's a fact.

NO NECK

(Jokingly) Agreed, all head chefs are bastards. You're a bastard, always have been always will. A total and utter bastard with no morals, soul or conscience. And last but in no way means least a fucking massive ego. I've always said you were a bastard from the moment we met and you know me I like everyone.

FAT HEAD

So Big Buller's restaurant gets a visit from Michelin. We knock our pan in. A bib, maybe even a star. Big Buller's takes the glory. What a day it's going to be. I hate Wednesdays. I need out of this place.

NO NECK

Exactly and you have a way better chance of getting finance to get out if you get a star. You know it and I know it. It has to be done. Get the star, get out to fuck, be your own man. Your name above the door. You can do it.

FAT HEAD

If only. Should of done it years ago.

NO NECK

Should of, would of, could of. All in the past, this is the present. Let's do it, let's show them. Get the star, get out to fuck, get your own place, get me on board as your sous chef.

FAT HEAD

Not you.

NO NECK	Not me, what do you mean not me.
FAT HEAD	Not you, not using you in my place as a sous chef.
NO NECK	Why not?
FAT HEAD	Because I am a bastard that's why.

They laugh and as they do NO NECK's shoulders life up high as his head sinks, making him look like he has NO NECK.

NO NECK	Piss off. Right, it's in the book, so, any change's on the menu chef.
FAT HEAD	Not sure.
NO NECK	*(In a French accent.)* We could go with thee classic French, *(in an Italian accent)* or traditional and simple Italian with the best of ingredients just like mama used to make, *(strong Belfast accent)* or indeed your standard Ulster menu with a bit of everything, providing the customer with plenty of reasons to piss and moan to everyone they met tomorrow after leaving a ten per cent tip and telling us 'it was lovely', just like every other restaurant in this town.
FAT HEAD	Not sure, fuck it, not adding anything. Fuck, I don't know.
NO NECK	Have you seen the rest of the bookings?
FAT HEAD	I have

NO NECK	So you know who is in then?
FAT HEAD	Inspection from Michelin, that blogger, and handful of regulars. And her.
NO NECK	She is in every couple of weeks now.
FAT HEAD	Leave it, alright, just leave it.
NO NECK	Just saying, just putting it out there.
FAT HEAD	Well just don't. It's over.
NO NECK	Doesn't have to be, you could always go back.
FAT HEAD	Never. Gone. All gone.
NO NECK	Sure. Doesn't mean you were wrong to go, just mean's things have changed. Things change.
FAT HEAD	They do, we get on, end off. Easier to get on, that's it, makes it easier.
NO NECK	Just saying.
FAT HEAD	You've said.
NO NECK	I did.
FAT HEAD	You did.

RUSTY enters

NO NECK	Big day Rusty, it's a big day!
RUSTY	Is it in the book?
NO NECK	It's in the book.
RUSTY	Pencil, pen or both?
NO NECK	Pen, aye pen. What do you mean both?
RUSTY	Both, what do you mean what do I mean. I mean both. Pencil, pen or both?
NO NECK	What odds?
RUSTY	Plenty odds. Pencil is pencil, pen is pen, both is both. Simple question. Pencil, pen or both?
NO NECK	Pen, told you, pen.
FAT HEAD	Wait. Both. It's both.
NO NECK	What odds, it's in the book. It's in pen in the book. That means it's happening. What odds if its pencil and pen.
RUSTY	Plenty odds.
FAT HEAD	Rusty is right No Neck, plenty odds.

RUSTY	Pencil is provisional and pen is confirmed. It's both. Means a provisional booking followed by a confirmation off the provisional booking. Definitely him? Are we sure it is definitely him?
NO NECK	So they say. Facebook. Twitter. That's what they are saying, that is the name he is using.
RUSTY	Says who?
FAT HEAD	Good point, says who? Coffee?
RUSTY	Usual.
NO NECK	Says everyone. Facebook. Twitter. Frankie Fuck Fuck texted me the other night. It's him. Frankie got caught out this day last week by him. Wednesday! Who reviews on a Wednesday?
FAT HEAD	Heard that too Rusty. Frankie Fuck Fuck let his guard down, cut a few corners, got caught out last Wednesday.
RUSTY	Not like Frankie to cut corners. You drinking cappuccino?
FAT HEAD	Exactly, its tough times, you know yourself, temptation is always there to cut corners in tough times.
NO NECK	Fancied something different.

RUSTY	No good cutting corners, tuff times or no, cutting corners is no good. Too much milk in a cappuccino for me, espresso, anything else is just shite.
NO NECK	I fancied a change. And we have all done it, trim here trim there, we have all done it. Frankie got unlucky.
RUSTY	Trimming corners is one thing, cutting is another. Well if that's what they say, then that's what they say. So, what are we doing, who is in?
NO NECK	It's Wednesday, so us three and Spoof.
RUSTY	Spoof, good, young Paddy Spoof is what you need on a day like today. Creative, he delivers.
FAT HEAD	Is he fuck, none of shite today. I can't take it, not today. I can't be having it.
NO NECK	Take him with a pinch of salt Fat Head. He is good, full of shite, but he is good, no harm in him.
RUSTY	He is better than good, a lot like you when you first walked in here Fat Head.
FAT HEAD	Fuck all like me. I had respect, manors, discipline. You made sure of that Rusty.

RUSTY | You were a cheeky wee bastard. You did your own thing and listened to no one. A right pain in the arse until you focused and mastered the classics. That's all Spoof needs, to focus, and master the classics.

NO NECK | A wee bastard he was then and a big bastard he is now. I have been telling him that all morning Rusty, telling you all morning I have. You're a bastard Fat Head, always were, always will be. That's what it will say on your gravestone. One word. Bastard. Everyone will know exactly who is planted six feet below. So menu, any change to the menu.

FAT HEAD | I can't have Spoof talking shit in my ear all day, not today, he just doesn't stop. Keep him away from me.

NO NECK | But he is good Fat Head, you can't say that he is not good. The kid can knock out some great food at the drop of a hat, you have to give him that.

RUSTY | Good, an honest chef.

FAT HEAD | What? Honest? You having a giraffe.

RUSTY | Honest chef, not truthful, but honest and good.

FAT HEAD Ok so he is good, but he doesn't listen. He called round to the house on Sunday night. I mean Sundays aren't a day for calling round to people's houses. I couldn't get rid of him. I even offered him a second cup of tea to see if that would do the trick and he took it.

NO NECK So what's the problem, you offered, he took it.

FAT HEAD On a Sunday? A second cup of tea on a Sunday! I don't know about your house, but in my house when you get asked do you want another cup of tea, it doesn't mean do you want another cup of tea. In my house, do you want ANOTHER cup of tea means any chance you can get the fuck out, you have had one cup now fuck off and stay away from my jammy dodgers. Wee bastard took it.

RUSTY Not like you to be shy? You going soft from you left Eileen.

FAT HEAD I didn't leave she wanted me gone. And I had the kids round, couldn't tell him to get the fuck out. I tried everything, even turned the heat off and opened the windows, he just kept on spoofing his load.

RUSTY He is in today. He is good, that's all that counts. Visit from Michelin can be a game changer. You know it, I know it, and Spoof will know it. Now focus, menu, what's the menu.

FAT HEAD   I think the taster works well, maybe, I don't know.

NO NECK   It works great. Leave it as it is. He will have looked at it already and will know what it is.

RUSTY   He is right Fat Head, the taster menu is great, our best seller, don't touch it. Just need to look at the rest, just in case or are you happy with it as it is?

NO NECK   Do we need something with a twist or a hook?

RUSTY   Why does everything now have to have a twist or a hook?

FAT HEAD   Just the way things have went

Paddy Spoof enters

SPOOF   Alright lads, what a day, big day what.

NO NECK   It is Spoof, big day.

RUSTY   Big day all right young Patrick. We need to focus.

SPOOF   Is it in the book.

FAT HEAD   Pencilled and penned.

SPOOF   Happy days.

RUSTY	We are looking at the menu now Paddy, time to focus.
SPOOF	You doing coffees Fat Head?
FAT HEAD	Yea.
SPOOF	I will have a grandee, skinny, ginger bread latte, with cinnamon sprinkles, and a drop of cream.
FAT HEAD	You can have an espresso or you can fuck off.
SPOOF	Well that's just lovely, how come No Neck gets a cappuccino?
FAT HEAD	Because I like him.
RUSTY	Put a drop of water in the espresso for him. We need to focus Paddy. Menu. Need to focus.
SPOOF	Absolutely, focus, that's me, Mr focus from focus street, focus town. Did you get the text from Frankie fuck fuck No Neck?
NO NECK	I did, how'd you know.
SPOOF	Did he tell you?
NO NECK	He did, how'd you know.
SPOOF	Seen him Sunday night in the bar, gutted he was. Sitting around with every other miserable looking git in that back bar pissing and moaning about work. How unfair it was. I stayed for one pint and left.

RUSTY	Menu Fat Head. Any additions. Focus Paddy need to focus son.
SPOOF	I know. Focus. Right. I am on it. I broke up with her last night.
FAT HEAD	Oh for the love of fuck, that's it.
SPOOF	I think I love her. I'd shaved my balls and everything.
NO NECK	Shaved your balls?
SPOOF	It's not easy being on the market these days, all change from when you were running about. Women want a well-groomed man. So I got out my Gillette fusion, gave it the lad a short back and sides. Scrubbed myself clean with that tea tree shower gel, know the one with the minty bits in it. I tell you what that squares you up.
FAT HEAD	Is this happening? Are we really having this conversation?
SPOOF	Anyway, the boys are sparkling, shiny and new. I do my usual, drop two Viagra about an hour before she is due to call round.
RUSTY	Viagra? You're a young man what the hell are you doing taking Viagra.

SPOOF	There is a lot of pressure on men to deliver sexually these days. In case you haven't noticed woman rule the world. Anyway, there's me, like a baby's arm holding an apple, ready to go at it. I was in good form, confident. I reckoned I could give her rampant rabbit a run for its money.
RUSTY	Her rampant what?
NO NECK	Don't ask
SPOOF	She walks in. I can tell something is up. She stripes off and I notice she is not matching, her underwear I mean.
NO NECK	That can be disappointing.
FAT HEAD	You see what I mean he is at it already. Is there something wrong with him? Is there something wrong with you?
SPOOF	Black bra, white pants, not good. If she can't be bothered to get a matching set you know you're on the road to ruin. I mean come on to fuck, how hard is it to make the effort.
RUSTY	For the love of God. Fat Head, menu, what's the menu?
FAT HEAD	Right the taster menu is good.

RUSTY	Better than good.
NO NECK	It's great.
SPOOF	Fucking belter it is.
FAT HEAD	We are all agreed the taster doesn't get touched.
SPOOF	We will need something with a hook or a twist. Deconstructed. Bit of foam, a drop of dry ice, a couple of fireworks.
FAT HEAD	None of that shit, just need to look at the rest of the dish's and make sure they are bang on.
RUSTY	A few more classics might be worthwhile.
SPOOF	Twist, need a twist, need to break it down and build it up again, that's what everyone does.
NO NECK	He has got a point.
FAT HEAD	I hate that shit, but he has got a point.
RUSTY	Classics. If you want to get your talent recognised you do the classics, a classic text that has lasted over time. You do something new, they don't know if it's your skill or you just got lucky. Everyone knows the classics.
SPOOF	How about a fry, doesn't get more classic than that.
NO NECK	A fry?

SPOOF   Yes, a fry with a twist. We make a soda bread,
               potato bread, and veda bread compote. Served
               with a bacon and sausage ice cream, we hang
               a bit of black pudding from a rope above the
               table, then on a side dish we do a baked bean
               foam, and we give him an uncooked raw egg
               with a small cooker and pan, tell him he can
               fucking cook it himself. He will love it. Bingo,
               we get a star, write a book and get fucking
               minted.

FAT HEAD   You ever say anything like that again in my
               presence, and I am going to beat you around the
               ankles with a lump hammer.

What I knew

Stephen Cunningham

Chapter One

19/11/2011

I need a dome. An impregnable, soundproof bubble, its glass ten inches thick. It will have a sign nailed to it—**DISTURB AT YOUR OWN RISK!** the sign will say. And let a moat surround this dome, thrashing with crocodiles, and these crocodiles will have photon cannons strapped to their backs, powerful enough to fire down a plane ten thousand miles high. And a wall! I need a wall to protect this moat. Granite five feet thick, mighty enough to laugh in the face of tanks. Archers will scout the wall—left-right, left-right—peeking from their towers, arrows poised and soaked with venom. And past hundreds of miles of scorched desert and burning sandstorms and chalked bones … let there be an electric fence, crackling with a million volts, powerful enough to vaporise anything that so much as sneezes at it. Then, and only then, *maybe*, I will be able to *write* something.

I wasn't five minutes in my cubbyhole—writing jotter open, water bottle filled, banana on the floor—when Patrick exploded in and leaned on the frame, clearly bored and looking for someone to annoy.

'Alright,' he said, and slurped his Guinness. 'What's with the face on *you*?'

I closed my jotter. 'I'm working!'

'*I'm workin*!' he mimicked in a foghorn voice. I've heard myself recorded back—reading my stories aloud, listening for syntactical faults—and I sound nothing like that. '*Ugh, my name's Peter and I'm like, ugh, tryin to write my wee book so I am, and, ugh, the whole world needs die so I can have quiet. Ugh.*'

He continued to slurp, smirking.

It was not the first time he flounced in while I was writing, and it will not be the last. My brother has no idea of concentration we writers must build, letting the colours of reality bleed off until there is only a blank canvas on which we paint our world. That idyllic scene—images, beautiful and vivid, roosting on the branches of your mind; ideas blossoming; a river of syntactically perfect words flowing onto the page—is as delicate as a soap bubble. It only takes one prick to pop it.

Patrick is a reality TV junkie. Craggy-faced bounty hunters, batty house cleaners, men valuing the crap in someone's attic, he shovels it all into his brain.

He is also extraordinarily hairy. His hairs grow hairs. They sprout from his bellybutton like a dried-up well and climb his torso in this coarse bramble. I occasionally wonder if he's invaded by something—if the hairs are a kind of parasite or worm, conquering his body one pore at a time.

He used to be the assistant manager of Argos. That ended two months ago, when he called the actual manager, an Italian Mr Fattarsi, 'Mr Fatass'. I don't remember what sparked the insult. Usually when Patrick bitches about his ex-job I'm off on some pillowy daydream, connecting the threads of my first novel.

I think I will talk about it. God knows nobody else wants to.

The Perfect Criminal it is called. *If* I had a pre-written blurb, it would be this:

John Dough [working name], an orphan of The Troubles, wandered the streets at the ages of five, seven, nine, pilfering food and money.

Now an adult, he makes a living by stealing on behalf of others. One night, however, he completes a job which crosses the bounds of his morality. Now he finds himself trapped in an escalating nightmare. He will soon learn that, in securing the life he wants, he will pay a high price...

I was a hundred words in when Patrick planted dynamite on my door and blew it off its hinges, sucking out the vacuum of peace and flooding in the sound of the washing machine, an auction on TV, laughing seagulls, hammers and chisels and hydraulic drills from a renovation next door, and the baby in the *other* next door—'WAAHHH! WAAHHH!'—and the mother cheering it up—'WHEEEE! WHEEEE! BAA BAA BLACK SHEEP HAVE YOU ANY *WOOOOOOL?*' Where are those construction headphones? Until I find them (and trust me, I've torn the house apart) my only defence is a paper doorhanger: Jack Nicholson baring his teeth through an axe-smashed door, under him the dripping red letters, KEEP OUT.

Patrick bore news. 'Kirsty Barker called.'

My jaw dropped, shattering on the floor. 'What?'

Patrick rested his chin smugly on the jamb.

'Kirsty ... She's not back from England, is she?' I said.

'Aye.'

'What did she say?'

'She asked if you were in.'

'And what did you say?'

'I said you were out.'

'Out? Out where?'

'Work.'

'Patrick...' I swallowed. 'You didn't tell her *where* I work, did you?'

Patrick's face went vacant. His sleepy lids shot up like blinds.

I banged my head on the desk. 'Why? *Why* did you *do* that?'

'Sorry, Pete, I wasn't thinkin.'

I sobbed, 'You do know she's going to be there every day, don't you? Every day she's going to be waltzing into Bookwarts, her and that stupid dog…'

For anyone who happens to read this diary, let me present to you Kirsty Barker. A girl like that demands her own paragraph break—*with a heart.*

♥

Once upon a time, there was a frizzy-haired princess called Kirsty, who lived around the corner from a hapless young writer called Peter Dickson. One day, drunk and desperate with loneliness, Peter asked Kirsty out on a date. So it began: they watched movies, frequented restaurants, visited parks like a *normal* couple. This came as a surprise—and as a source of amusement—for many. Sporting garish rainbow-coloured tank tops and eyelashes like butterfly wings, and toting her Chihuahua, Mr Snuff, in a sequin-studded handbag, Kirsty was very much the talk of The Village.

But all was not as it seemed. Two weeks later, against Peter's knowledge, Kirsty soared across the seas on a majestic bird called Ryanair to sing in a famous TV talent show. The princess would do her Village proud, she thought. Her name would sparkle in Las Vegas, West End, the Waterfront—and every land would pay tribute to her, weep at her concerts, plead for her autograph.

Sporting the most garish tank top she could muster, and dressing Mr Snuff in a tux, she paraded onstage, the sound of her eyelashes flapping for miles around. The crowd fell silent. Taking a deep breath—calling upon the love, hurt, tears and betrayal she had suffered as a princess— she delivered an ear-perforating rendition of Whitney Huston's 'I Will Always Love You' and addressed to who else but Peter, her boyfriend of two weeks, not forgetting to blow him a kiss into the camera. Grimaces spread throughout the audience like an eggy fart. The three judges waved for the sound system to be turned off.

And so she waited for their verdict, eyes filled with hope and tears—'The song means so much to my boyfriend!' she blubbered to the judges. (Three months later, when Peter saw this air, he would faint, hitting his head against a table, needing three nasty stitches.)

The First Judge, the kindest judge, told her sorry, it was a no.

The Second Judge, when she stopped laughing, said sorry, but no also.

Then the camera turned to the Third Judge, the meanest, cruellest judge there ever was. Kirsty implored him with her eyes. If only he said yes! Surely he had to say yes, for the world of Kirsty Barker was a dream, a fantasy concocted in her own head.

He said, 'That was utterly abysmal.'

And so Kirsty flew back on Ryanair, never to sing again.

Afterwards, during a period known as The Great Embarrassment, Peter Dickson would not leave his house. People used to come from far and wide to laugh at Peter—'Mummy! Mummy! Is that the man the funny girl talked about on TV?' 'Yes, sweetheart, don't point at him.' The relationship ended, of course, but to this day Kirsty still calls. Any time between 5:00 p.m. and 9:00 p.m., when her shift ends in McDonald's—and if you watch carefully—you can see Kirsty knock on the door of Peter's terrace house on University Avenue. And if you watch *really* carefully, you can see Peter dropping out of view of the window, or squashing himself against the back of the settee. And if you watch *really really* carefully, the resident troll, Patrick, might answer the door—'Shoo, frizzy princess! Shoo!' It is this very Patrick who told Kirsty where Peter worked, so she will live happily ever after, tormenting Peter 'til the end of his days…

♥

'Sorry,' said Patrick again, his eyes scouring the floor as if for words. I felt a little bad. Despite his blunder, he actually did me a favour, warning me about Kirsty.

'Forget it,' I said. I placed my hands on my jotter, hoping he'd take the hint. He slurped his Guinness one last time and closed the door.

So here I am, penning my diary by the light of a halogen lamp in the cubbyhole under the stairs. Every so often Patrick thump, thump, thumps overhead, leaving a chase scene blaring in the living room. The baby, one wall away, is still crying, and the mother's squealing it to sleep— 'HUMPTY DUMPTY SAT ON A WALL! HUMPTY DUMPTY HAD A GREAT *FAAAAAALLLL...*' I close my eyes and breathe—breathe, Peter, I tell myself. I eat my banana, drink my water and breathe. Slowly, cautiously, sceptically, concentration returns: Images flutter back to their branches. Ideas resume their blossoming. And the river, a trickle at first, begins to flow again

Great, now my bloody pen   running out, the

[Acknowledgement is given to the Arts Council NI which, through the National Lottery, funded the following novel in its entirety as part of their Support For the Individual Artist Programme.]

Start Here

Patrick McFarlane

I am conducting a detailed review
of the 90,000 emails and texts
he sent or received, using company
hardware or via his work address,
between September 08 and now
which feature the search term 'press'.

'Press' is traders' shorthand for 'press
down the interbank rate' and a review
of the stats suggests he did this now
and then – though he sent most of his texts
from a phone registered at his home address
which we can't get hold of through the company.

But to keep to our agreement with the company
to settle this case by August, I must press
on, while making sure I address
each message properly: the key to the review
isn't the wording of these emails and texts
but their significance given what we know now.

What I am hoping to discover now
is evidence of a network outside the company:
people he sent these untraceable texts
so they could manipulate the rate. I press
'Show Next'. Up for review
is an email titled 'Change of Address'.

I hope it's not about a change of address
but it is. I do 500 and now
I get an alert titled 'Krypton Review'
(Krypton isn't the name of the company,
it's a code name) and see that the press
have got their hands on a batch of his texts

and are poring over his dirty texts
('bring poppers n lube – heres my address')
and it's hard to believe as I glance through the press
that considering the world we live in now
he never once imagined that his company
would agree to submit his emails for review

or that despite deletion you could review texts.
And why did he use his company address?
But now I press on, and now press -

Show Next

Patrick McFarlane

I am the front runner in the JP Morgan
2015 Hong Kong Ultramarathon.
The course is about 50 kilometers long
stretching from one end of Lung Wo Road
to the other end of Lung Wo Road, and back
and forth, 25 times down and back
earning the winner the title of JP Morgan
2015 Iron Champion. 'The road
to the top is hard,' said my first ultramarathon
coach – he had been doing them too long
and had had a small heart attack, but as long
as you take a bit of care you can get back
into it, that's the beauty of the ultramarathon.
It's sad that after last year JP Morgan
didn't want any trouble with lots of road
blocks, so now the course is just this one road,
Lung Wo Road, which is only a kilometre long.
Though even before, I've noticed at JP Morgan
most people, whether it's their knees or back,
can only manage one ultramarathon.

This year is my fifth ultramarathon.
It's funny you know when you all you can see is road
you just long for a chair but you need to bring yourself back
to the point of all this and you keep thinking: not long
now and you'll be back at your desk at JP Morgan.

Show Next

Patrick McFarlane

I'm out for a drink with someone I met online.
We agree how boring dates usually are.
Yes! I know what you mean – time after time.

By which I mean every time. This time
we share some serrano ham at a tapas bar.
We kiss outside and get a cab to mine.

This time it's cocktails with silver tequila and lime.
I look at those pressed lips and know what you're after –
yes, I know. What, you mean time after time?

Yes. This time it's coffee; home by nine
but I know you'll leave the door to a drink ajar.
We kiss outside and get a cab to mine.

This time it's just a pub but you make a sign
at your glass and ask 'Do we have time after?'
(Yes I know!) What? You mean time after...? Time

for another glass? But you say, 'I've had enough wine
if you know what I mean. I mean – is your flat far?'
Yes, I know what you mean. Time after time
we kiss outside and get a cab to mine.

Show Next

Patrick McFarlane

I go to Tesco to do my weekly shop.
I withdraw ten pounds from the machine.
I get a basket from the front of the shop,
making sure I pick one that's clean.

I withdraw ten pounds from the machine
(ten is not enough). I select an aubergine
making sure I pick one that's clean,
then I bag some mushrooms (about fifteen:

ten is not enough). I select an aubergine
remembering that Fiona is coming tomorrow,
then I bag some mushrooms (about fifteen)
and two peaches which I turn all over and blow.

Remembering that Fiona is coming tomorrow
I look for some pudding: double cream
and two peaches which I turn all over and blow,
as if there's something I haven't seen.

I look for some pudding: double cream
and a triple chocolate pot that's HALF PRICE
as if there's something I haven't seen.
I think a decent voucher this week would be nice,

and a triple chocolate pot that's half price.
You won't lose out. And when I'm asked for money
I think a decent voucher this week would be nice
which gives me 31 pence off and entitles me:

YOU won't lose out. And when I'm asked for money
the first thing I'll do is get out last week's voucher
which gives me 31 pence off and entitles me
to credit my Club Card with everything I've bought here.

The first thing I'll do is get out last week's voucher
(once again I remind myself). I find it very satisfying
to credit my Club Card with everything I've bought here:
it's never long before I need to go shopping

once again. I remind myself I find it very satisfying.
I get a basket from the front of the shop:
it's never long before I need to go shopping.
I go to Tesco to do my weekly shop.

Personal Collection

Patrick McFarlane

I am a sword with a brown blade
and a brown crown for a pommel, made
by an Ottoman smith for a nameless Ottoman,
mounted here by an Irish gentleman
opposite another sword, above
assorted daggers, above an alcove
in which a chunk of hieroglyphic
rock is set like an off-colour brick.

I am the bed of a Burmese Queen.
And this is the moon, my mistress, seen
hours before her removal, shown
standing to the side of her empty throne.
I am a letter from the Queen-Empress.
She hopes you will not be unimpressed
when she asks for a bag of Burman jewels
like the ones she got when we annexed Oude.

I am a bust of the god Amun,
brought to light in an Ulster tomb.
I am a ball-headed axe. I'm told
I am one of just two in the world.

I am part of a Speke's gazelle.
I am a Maharajah's tricycle.
I am a polished elephant's foot.
I am Mentuhotep's foot.

I am a bead bag, sewn by a Canadian
before Canada was finalised. I contain
nothing, see? Anyone is free
to lift the flap. Nothing is within me.
On my front is a familiar brand:
a coroneted monogram
carefully placed by a subject nation
in a clearing within its pattern.

5 March 2015

Patrick McFarlane

I blow out a candle on my cake
as the sun goes down for the last time
on the ruins of Nimrud's ziggurat.
In a museum on YouTube, men take
hammers to cuneiform, hack lime
mortar with axes, power-tool flat
the human face of a winged bull.

They are making new records:
houses marked N for Nazarene,
whitewashed rooms where a girl will miss
the familiar bears her father hoards
on an unmade bed in Bethnal Green
and try to enjoy the curious kiss
of a Swedish boy with a heavy beard.

I'm not her, yet still I see
the coloured hoardings telling all
women to keep their faces covered.
Still I see the headless body
tied to a dusty post and the scrawl
beneath explaining they'd discovered
he used to be a street magician.

Acts of Rebellion

Jonathan Vischer

It was the year that Donegal won the cup. For ages southern counties like Cork and Kerry had dominated Gaelic football and then – unbelievably – it was the Northwest's turn to shine.

'Feeney's the man,' she had said. Sean Feeney was not only the captain but also the playmaker for the Donegal team. In a sport that demanded peak levels of fitness and stamina from its players Feeney was the tactical brain that had landed The Sam Maguire for Donegal. Frank imagined the great silver cup as it toured the local schools. From Ballyshannon to Malin town, boys and girls wanted to touch its polished surface - to bask in its reflected glory.

For Frank Doherty early retirement had come at a cost. Freed from the daily commute to Letterkenny, he had been forced to face the stark reality of his marriage to Maeve. Pussy-whipped was a phrase that had been used down in Rodden's Bar. Hen-pecked was an expression that an earlier generation might have chosen. For Frank, retirement meant exactly that: retirement to his workshop beyond the house. It was within these confines that he now spent most of his time. This was a masculine space: in it he had constructed a world of routers, sanders and bench-saws. Then, separate from the woodworking equipment, his real pride and joy - shelves of polishes and shellacs. Anything used to oil, stain and finish wood could be found in this work- space. For Frank, few

experiences could match watching a pale spindle soak up an even coat
of varnish to leave its grain tanned to translucent depth.

Inishowen Partnership. The organisation had provided a second
career for his wife and had probably wrecked his marriage. It was
fourteen months ago - after Maeve had gained a seat on the board - that
he had noticed a marked change in her attitude towards him. In spite
of his own pension and hard-won savings he was now seen almost as
a dependent. Maybe, it would all have been different if they had had
children. Who knows: perhaps it was 'the change'? Whatever the cause,
it was clear to him that real respect was in short supply. His was no
longer a marriage of equals. Yesterday, he had overheard a conversation
between his wife and Sheena from the golf club.

Sheena: 'What does he do in that shed of his all day?'

Maeve: 'He futters - he doesn't really make *anything*, you know.'

Sheena: 'And what's that smell?'

Maeve: 'Beetlejuice.'

Sheena: 'What?'

Maeve: 'French polish - it's made from crushed beetles.'

Sheena: 'I'll never eat off a fancy table again.'

Maeve: 'He's inhaled that much of the stuff - it's like he's full half
the time; the other half he's just crabby.'

Frank stepped outside his front door and regarded the cyclists who
glided by to Muff and Moville. These days the roads were alive with
their brightly coloured lycra - slim grasshopper legs pedaling impossibly
light machines around the bends of the Inishowen One Hundred.

He turned away from the road to face the bull. The stupidity of it still
made him wince. Every other house in the county was decked out with
yellow and green flags and yet his home - sorry villa - had a life-size
Spanish bull standing outside. It was black; it was bovine.

'His thrust is grievous. No soft thing to stand him. Rude will be
the wound.' The boys had quoted Ferdiad in the pub. Frank tapped the
bull's fiberglass body. It sounded hollow like an empty collection box.

High above the tree line, a narrow row of white cottages stood in silent rebuke. The dwellings belonged to the Grants who had farmed these rocky slopes for generations. Frank could pick out Mickey's house - a small trail of turf smoke was rising from its chimney. Mickey was the real thing: a stockman who worked a fourteen-hour day and rarely had a bad word to say about anyone.

The idea for the bull had come from a story by the Andalusian writer Carlos Zubias. It was more than five years since Maeve's literary group had selected his historical novel *La Pata Negra* for their book of the month. A series of holidays to Seville and Granada had followed and gradually their house had transformed itself with terracotta and tiles. Now it resembled a gift shop on the Camino de Santiago.

Zubias' phrase *La Pata Negra* translated literally as *the black sow*.

'But why a bull?' Frank had asked, exasperated when Silicon Eire had delivered the plastic effigy - obscenely mounted on the back of the company's pick-up truck.

'They don't do boars, besides a bull has more presence, don't you think?' She had laughed, enjoying his discomfort and the absurdity of it all. In Andalusia, a black pig carried with it notions of the highest quality. In Donegal the presence of a large plastic bull by the roadside suggested a café serving wine, although probably not from Porto or Jerez. Either way Maeve perceived the animal's presence as a mark of status. Other people sported a pair of eagles on their gateposts; she marked the spot with 'el toro'. It wasn't too much to ask for, was it?

Back in his workshop, Frank clandestinely unpacked his secret stash of books. This was not, as Maeve suspected, some personal collection of pornography but part of the fight-back.

'Fight fire with fire,' somebody had once advised and that was exactly what he intended to do. He selected *Dream of the Celt* by Mario Vargas Llosa. Turning the title over, he read the blurb written by The Nobel Prize committee. It recommended the book for 'its cartography of structures of power and its trenchant images of an individual's resistance and revolt.' Then the volume fell open to reveal its clever secret. Hidden in its centre was the book within the book - transfers of twenty-two carat gold leaf. Each square of gold was cushioned between two pages of peach tissue. Frank checked that he was alone before reverently opening the tiny pages. His face lit up with a rich lustre. The leaves measured five centimetres square, yet each contained no more than a pinhead of pure, unadulterated metal. They were rolled so thin that they could float on the slightest breeze and couldn't be felt when scrumpled between finger and thumb. Gold changed people - Frank knew this. This wasn't just a money thing: gold affected the nervous system, directly. He had witnessed the changes wrought by the metal himself. Gold was power.

Frank's interest in precious metals had been re-ignited by a documentary he caught on the Discovery Channel. The piece had charted the history of civilizations through alloys and smithying before throwing out the mind-blowing fact that gold and other trace elements were all around us. Seawater - it turned out - contained huge quantities of the metal, which was distributed widely across the world's oceans. As a child, Frank had watched sign painters on Shipquay Street in Derry applying gold leaf; now he was determined to experiment with the metal himself.

'A little man with tiny balls,' Frank whispered.

Maeve was not impressed.

'Frank Doherty - that's most unkind. If Colum McLoughlin wants to caddie for his wife on Lady's Day, then who are you to judge him?'

'The man's spineless.' He had not meant to speak with such venom. He decided to keep his powder dry and say no more.

'Well, he, Sheena and all the girls will be coming back here on Saturday.'

'Here, on Saturday?' Frank felt a shiver of anticipation run up his spine.

'Yes, Saturday after the tournament. I've invited them in for tapas and rioja. I do hope you can be pleasant. Colum has expressed an interest in French polishing - you can show him around your workshop.'

Frank smiled, 'No problem.' She looked a little surprised at his sudden compliance. Unsure, she checked that the bowls of olives were still untouched in the fridge.

'You could help me by setting out the tables. If the weather's good we'll eat alfresco.'

'What are the chances of that?' he thought to himself, but he, too, was hoping for good weather.

As it happened Saturday dawned almost cloudless. Watching the sun as it rose above Lough Foyle, Frank found himself speculating about the weight of gold bars contained within its body of water. Once the idea gripped you it was hard to free yourself. It occurred to him that he had been spending too much time alone. It didn't do to brood and yet he had never been close to his work colleagues and he didn't much fit in with the regulars in Rodden's Bar, either. He tried to picture Maeve as she was when he had first met her. He missed her - the slender girl with eager eyes that blinked a little too often. Somehow, the one he loved had been swallowed up by that oversize body with its flabby arms and sour wit - La Pata Blanca. Not that *he* was anything to write home about these days - still, he was working on that.

'Home at six: there should be eight of us, including Colum. You could give the house a hoover and arrange the sun loungers on the decking.' She loaded her golf clubs into the minibus and rummaged in her bottomless bag.

She handed him a short but precise shopping list.

He glanced at it briefly, 'Soda for spritzers.' He read, 'Chorizo? That required a drive through Grainne's Gap to Buncrana - ridiculous.'

After Maeve had departed, Frank took off his wedding ring and rolled it in the palm of his hand. How many books of gold leaf could be made with its weight? He imagined the front door of the house reflecting the sun like a solid ingot. Above it a small blue circle of ceramic announced, 'Here lived Frank and Maeve Doherty 1982 – 2018. Frank made his millions on the bullion markets. Maeve collected pedigree bulls.'

A car horn broke into his reverie; it was Donal from the petrol station. Frank waved brightly. He slipped the ring back onto his finger and made his way through the house. He picked up a bottle of surgical spirit from the downstairs toilet and pulled off a wad of cotton wool from the workshop. On his way back through the living room, he noticed a hardback edition of Zubias' latest bestseller lying on the coffee table. He prodded open the fly-leaf and perused the black and white photo of the author. A laconic face with a trim goatee looked back at him. The author appeared suitably Latin but he could be anyone, for God's sake. Writers used pen names - why not invent a whole identity? In any case, there was an audience of menopausal women out there and they would believe exactly what they wanted to believe. Once he was outside, Frank settled down on his haunches by the bull's flank.

'He's probably a mate of Daniel O'Donnell. I bet they play golf together on Owey Island. Coining it in - he must be.' Frank felt the pungent sting of surgical spirit on his blistered fingers and reached forward to swab the black scrotum that hung between the bull's hind legs. He waited for the volatile mixture to evaporate, before applying a coat of oil-based varnish onto the oversize testicles. This was three-hour size: it would be tacky enough to receive gold leaf by midday, he calculated.

After helping himself to a generous lunch of olives, artichokes and patatas bravas, Frank checked the commodities markets on Allied Irish. com. Greeted by a series of red losses, he skim-read a post entitled *Bad News for Gold Bugs* before shaking off the notion that the long bull-run was over.

'Los cohones dorados.' He mouthed to himself as he tested the gloss surface with his little finger. The gold transfer flashed in the sunlight and for a moment Frank was aware that he might be seen from the road. Then, like a true craftsman, he settled to his task - coaxing the thin foil from its paper backing onto the rounded contours of the fibreglass ball sack. The job was trickier than he had imagined. The leaf tore easily and the uppermost areas of varnish appeared to be drying quicker than the base. Frank watched as slivers of twenty-two carat gold blew away across his neighbour's garden. They floated like shreds of solid sunshine before catching on the hydrangea bushes.

'¿Son todo mentiras - las palabras del escritor dorado?'[1]

Frank pictured Zubias' portrait in his mind. His work was almost done. Smoothing down a few loose edges of leaf with cotton wool, he cleared the ground underneath the bull with a small hand-held Dyson. It had been a birthday present from Maeve and this was the first time he had used it. He pulled away the masking tape and admired his handy work. The glister of gonads stood out against the matt black underneath of the bull.

'Simple but effective,' he thought.

* * *

The minibus disgorged its slightly tipsy crew and Frank stood out at the front of the house to greet them.

'How did you get on?'

Maeve was brimming with goodwill.

'Star of the day was definitely Sheena – she birdied the last three holes.'

Sheena looked impossibly content.

'I couldn't have done it without my coach and confidant, Colum.'

'Let me get those.' Frank unloaded Maeve's clubs and stood for a moment to enjoy the evening light. 'Nowhere else in the world,' he said wistfully, before ushering the party towards the decking.

---

1   'Are they all lies – the words of the gilded writer?'

'That's one fine specimen you have there.' Colum had paused to admire the bull.

'Extraordinary, isn't he?'

The sun was about to sink behind the hill: its rays caught on the underside of el Toro.

Sheena MacLoughlin knelt down to take a closer look. Her hand involuntarily reached out to cup the purse of gold. She looked up at Maeve.

'Is that solid?'

Frank was drinking in his wife's reaction. Maeve had taken a step back and was regarding the golden balls with a critical eye. She appeared unfazed.

'Frank's been *experimenting* with finishes: this is… just a sampler.' Ignoring his eyes, she surveyed the opinion of the group. 'What do you think: should we go the whole hog - so to speak?'

There was a murmur of appreciation. 'Powerful,' someone managed to say.

'I'd say that's decided, then Frank. He'll look wonderful when he's finished - very welcoming, like a great, golden hallo.'

The Follower

Kerry Millar

Rosie had never really believed they existed. She had heard of them sporadically on the television and occasionally (if she ever bothered to listen to it) on the radio. It was one of those things that she, and many others no doubt, heard about but didn't really think about. It was something that the famous and the attention seekers got.

Something needs to be done, they always said. Something needs to change so that the stigma can be erased. Rosie often turned the channels over when they talked for too long about it.

But then one appeared before her. A Follower. A presence, slightly different for everyone but apparently with the same effect. One night, Rosie saw a little dark blue form grow on the desk in her room. It swirled and wriggled like winter fog manipulated by a god's invisible hand.

It looked like a stubborn liquid — moving almost, but not quite, freely. It settled and became stronger in colour, remaining unbearably noiseless. On Rosie's desk, the Follower took its form. She could not fully make out what it had settled as, but it looked like a cat or a fox. Maybe a bit of both.

It had a head with two very straight and pointed ears rising directly up. Its body did not look furry, but smooth. Its skin looked like the night sky in some far away land. It was deep purple, with white dots that looked like little galaxies patterned all over. They definitely moved a little. Some faded in and some faded out as if shy of the other's presence. There were two silver splotches on the head that Rosie assumed were meant to resemble eyes, and around its belly were slow, snaking puffs of light purple smoke. She could only see the slender, paw-less front legs. The back ones — if there were any — were hidden under the smoke, which smelled of nothing.

Rosie looked at it from her bed, laptop resting on her thighs. The Follower looked back at her, betraying no expression. It looked around her room and got up, the smoke fluttering. It jumped, without a single noise, off her desk and onto her bed. Its motions were swift and graceful.

It made no dent on the sheets, and Rosie could not feel the disturbance when it padded its way over to her and looked around like a curious animal. There was no body heat from it, and there was no cool breeze. She had almost expected it to feel like a ghost.

She kept her eye on it, even as her laptop's screensaver came on. She thought about the celebrities who talked about it on those morning chat shows sometimes watched before Uni. The women would talk about their Follower and how it began to drag them down. They then realised that they needed help.

And one of these was sitting beside Rosie. A creature that could only be seen by the person it followed, and something others could only detect if they knew what they were looking for.

'What a load of crap,' Rosie muttered to herself in a cracked voice. 'You, my little friend, are going to leave me alone soon enough. Aren't you?'

She did not expect a verbal reply, but it still made her shoulders tense when it did not even nod.

She got up, placing her laptop on the bedside table. The essay could wait just a little bit.

Rosie took up her backpack and plopped it roughly on the desk where the Follower first appeared. She did not look around. Pushing the graduate jobs catalogue aside, she packed what she needed for the morning. She briefly thought about the people who complained about 9am lectures, and closed her eyes, breathing through her nose. Surely it wasn't the most unreasonable thing in the world to want someone to be somewhere for 9am?

The Follower jumped beside her backpack, and Rosie flinched. She stepped back, pulling the backpack with her and setting it on the floor.

She left her room, closing the door harder than she intended.

She made her way down the stairs, and on the landing, catching her eye, was the Follower.

In the kitchen, Rosie's mother was watching television. She gave her daughter her usual smile by way of greeting, and Rosie returned it tightly. She poured herself a glass of water, and when she put the jug back, she felt something light and airy brush against her legs. The Follower was slinking around the bottom of the drawers, keeping close to them. Rosie glanced over to her mother, whose attention was turned to the television. Something about people claiming benefits was on again.

'What's wrong?' her mother asked, looking over to her.

'Oh, nothing,' Rosie said.

'Are you sure?'

Rosie nodded and moved to the door. 'Yeah. Just getting ready for bed.'

'Good night.'

'Night.'

Rosie left the kitchen and walked back up the stairs, feeling suddenly drained. At least it was true. People couldn't see Followers unless they had one. Rosie could probably ignore this thing long enough to let it go away on its own. She again saw it on the landing, not quite paying attention to her, as it seemed fascinated by the light dangling from the ceiling.

Rosie brushed her teeth, trying not to look at herself in the mirror. She washed her face, got into bed, and closed her eyes.

And she wondered if Followers slept. It did not seem to breathe or blink, so her guess was that the thing just sat up all night staring at her.

And she realised that she could not sleep.

* * *

With dry, heavy eyes, Rosie got on the bus and took her seat somewhere in the middle. The Follower took a seat beside her and lay down with a stretch. It was the most pet-like thing she had seen it do. The purple smoke was slow as it lazily rolled around itself. Maybe Followers did get tired.

She set her backpack on her knees and hugged it lightly. She would never forget the time she set her bag on the floor by her feet and it got covered in the sticky goo of a child's lollipop. The Follower lay quietly beside her, staring at the people who got on at the stops. One lady turned her back to sit down, and Rosie glanced at the Follower, wondering what it would do.

It got up and jumped out of the lady's way. The smoke trailed behind it, making it look very snake-like. It hopped on to the luggage shelf and decided to walk along it. It was not looking at Rosie, instead walking up and down the long shelf in a slow, lethargic manner.

Her stop came, and Rosie apologetically squeezed past the lady and got off the bus. The noise of the campus was familiar, yet somehow it made her feel sick. She placed her hand over her stomach and walked to her building. The Follower was ever present, and Rosie wondered if she would be able to see it walk through walls. But her aim was, of course, to ignore it.

She walked up the stairs to her lecture room and took her seat. As usual, the room filled up before Amy made it in. Amy gave Rosie a quick, apologetic wave, and Rosie raised her hand back. Amy mouthed something and sat down in the front. The people either side of Rosie took out their laptops and clicked and tapped until they got their word documents open. The lecturer fumbled with his own laptop, bringing up the subject he would be talking about for the next two hours.

'Looks like most of us have made it,' he said, clapping his hands together. 'I don't have to waste the first fifteen minutes talking about you no-showers behind your backs, then!'

Some people chuckled. Rosie rolled her eyes, knowing it was the typical no-showers who were chuckling.

The Follower skipped along the table, avoiding any contact with Rosie's neighbours, and sat down, purple smoke partially covering Rosie's notebook. Her fingers twitched with the temptation to slap the Follower away. Instead, she craned her neck and began to write.

The laptops began to tick and tap rapidly.

When 11am creeped up, and everyone shuffled out of the room, Rosie held her hand to the back of her neck. She tried not to grit her teeth, but the muscle felt twisted. The Follower had not moved for the entire two hours, and sometimes the smoke plumed out, obstructing her view of the slides. Some of her writing was smudged and blotted, looking more like something shown in a psychiatrist's office.

'Hey Rosie! Sorry I was late,' Amy said, popping out of the crowd.

'Don't worry,' Rosie said in the tone she always said it in.

'I was wondering if you wanted to go shopping now. We don't have our tutorial until two, right?' She beamed at Rosie. 'I need a dress for this party tomorrow night.'

The Follower flittered in the corner of Rosie's eye. 'You still don't have an outfit for that? Why don't you wear something you already have?'

Amy clicked her tongue. 'Are you serious?'

Rosie glanced at the Follower. It was sitting on top of a pile of stacked chairs. It looked over the thinning crowd like some kind of little god.

'I guess I could come along,' Rosie said.

'Great! Maybe you can get something for yourself, too,' Amy said.

They walked out of the campus and down the streets. It was a bright morning, but obscured by the fact that it had rained the night before. Puddles needed to be dodged, and it spoiled the more spring-like sunshine.

'Are you ok?' Amy asked suddenly.

Rosie looked at her. 'Yeah, why?'

'You seem distracted,' she said.

The Follower was jumping carefree around the street. It occasionally leaped into a tree and sat there, waiting for the girls to pass under it, and then it would jump down and zip past Rosie's legs, just about touching them. It cast no shadow on the ground, and no reflection in the puddles.

'I'm fine. Just... a bit tired, I guess,' Rosie said.

'Late one?'

Rosie thought for a moment. 'I guess.'

They reached the centre of town, and Amy led Rosie wherever she needed to go. The shops were quiet, and Rosie was glad of it. She sat down and waited for Amy to try on a dress she picked out.

The Follower sat by Rosie's feet, now staring right up at her.

'Get lost,' Rosie said. 'You're starting to annoy me.'

It did not move, and it did not move even when Amy came out, twirling and asking Rosie's opinion.

'Is it too red?' Amy asked.

Rosie got up. 'It's lovely. Listen... I think I'll head back.'

'But we just got here.' Amy folded her arms.

'I know, I'm sorry. I just — There's work I need to do before the tutorial,' Rosie said.

'Ok,' Amy said. 'I'll see you at the tutorial, then?'

'Sounds good.'

When Rosie got into the library, and she saw the Follower take a seat beside her on the desk, she realised that she could not do any work. She realised that she was so tired that she could not think about taking notes or even highlighting. She could not enjoy the smell of old books and she could not bring herself to eat any lunch. Looking at the Follower, she began to feel more ill. The little galaxies coating its body were beginning to make her dizzy.

* * *

And as the weeks rolled by, hazily and sluggishly, Rosie always had one eye on her Follower. She felt weaker, as though someone was drinking the energy out of her. The Follower had taken to constantly brushing itself around Rosie's legs, and sit so close to her that she thought she could even smell it.

* * *

Taking a seat in tutorial, Rosie saw the smokey tail disappear under it. She wondered if it was looking up at her.

Amy had arrived too late to take a seat beside Rosie again, and sat at the opposite end of the room.

When it ended, and the lecturer told Rosie he wanted to hear more from her next time, she turned to pack up. The Follower jumped onto her bag, and she realised that this was the first time she could... really feel it. She breathed in sharply as she heard Amy call her, and with a quick sweep of her arm, she pushed the Follower into her backpack, zipping it up clumsily.

'Rosie! You coming to swimming later?'

'I, uh... No. I think I'll just head home.'

Amy's features creased into the same face people give a dog who will not cooperate on the lead. 'What is with you? You've been acting really strange, and frankly, it's been a bit of a bummer.'

Rosie shook her head and said weakly, 'I just… I'm just a little tired.'

The Follower was sitting outside the classroom, waiting like a spirit.

*   *   *

Trying to ignore the rolling purple smoke and the vacant, staring silver eyes, Rosie walked through the door. She contemplated stuffing the Follower into a cupboard, even while knowing that it would be a futile effort.

Her mother was in the kitchen, and greeted her.

'Good day?'

'Uh,' Rosie thought for a moment. 'Not really.'

'Why?'

'Just a bit tired.' Rosie raised her hand to her eyes, realising that tears were beginning to form. She blinked. 'It's just been really… rubbish lately.'

Her mother turned to her, not moving from the spot she stood on. Her eyes moved, and Rosie's heart sank when she realised that she was looking where the Follower sat, staring right back at her.

Rosie leaned against the counter, gripping the edge with shaking hands.

Her mother turned back to her, and blinked while giving her head a single, quick shake. 'Everyone has a bad day. Just cheer up, ok?'

Rosie wondered if her mother could see it, or if she only thought she saw something. Rosie glanced at the Follower, wondering if it was finally beginning to materialise as a part of her character. She felt her throat tighten.

'Ok, mum,' Rosie said.

'If you're feeling down, you need to find a way of snapping yourself out if it. You can't walk around being miserable all the time,' her mother continued.

Rosie left and went to her room. She sat down on the bed and drew her knees close to her chest. The Follower sat in front of her, ears pointed high and eyes pointed at her.

'I just need to... Sort myself out — Sort you out... I... I need to... Snap out of it...'

And Rosie buried her face in her folded arms, crying.

*　*　*

The streets were quiet, and Rosie was glad of the peace. She hardly knew where she was going, but somehow, all that mattered was that she was on her own and away from people who could only comment on her behavior.

The Follower had taken to scurrying like a cat, and it strayed out on to the road every now and then.

She looked up to the heavy sky, and spotted a lone bird. It flapped its wings awkwardly, and then vanished. Rosie blinked, wondering if it had disappeared into the clouds. Then it reappeared in a puff of smoke. The smoke was a deep blue, and it surrounded the bird's wings. It wasn't flying so much as it was hovering around one area.

Rosie looked ahead to see where it was, and she walked briskly, looking up to keep track of her direction. The bird did disappear from time to time, but it kept coming back.

She began to jog, and then run.

The streets got narrower and more cobbled, and the buildings began to shrink, giving way to a greenery. The park was planted among smaller shops and more intimate streets. Rosie remembered people talking about this place — a good place to study in favourable weather.

The bird swooped down and landed in a tree, shuddering and flexing. Its body was the same skinless colour as Rosie's Follower, except it was a darker hue of purple, and there were tiny, blinking white dots adorning it.

The benches were mostly vacant, until she spotted a man sitting alone. He was wearing a long sleeved t-shirt and jeans, and as Rosie approached him, she realised that he must have been about her age — he was probably a student.

He looked at her, and at the Follower, who was keeping close.

'Hello,' he said, smiling.

Rosie could not help but smile back. 'Hi.'

'I'm Connor.'

'Rosie.'

He nodded to the Follower. 'How long have you had that?'

'A few weeks… How long have you…?'

'A few years — but as you can see, it's not as strong as it once was.' Connor turned around and looked at it. 'See, it can barely keep form. There are weeks I go without seeing it at all.'

'How…?'

He smiled again. 'It helps to talk to someone who can see them. Even if it's just with someone who has a Follower themselves. If they can see them, they know how to help. *We* know what to look for.'

Rosie nodded. 'I haven't met anyone who could see them. I thought my mum could, but…'

'Some people can only vaguely see them, and they often dismiss it,' Connor said. 'They don't understand.'

The Follower stood back — further than it had been for weeks.

'They don't.'

'If you like, I can show you where there are other Followers. It helped me, and I bet it will help you.'

'Really?'

'It can take a while, but you can get rid of your Follower. You can feel free again.'

The Follower sat on a grassy mound, staring at them. The smoke rose into the air, thinning and disappearing.

Rosie smiled. 'I'd like to meet them.'

Estero Untended

Damien Laughlin

Three days he lay upon the tainted earth;
Three days gasped, wild eyed, the untended herd,
While darked the sun by clouds of sharp-beaked birds
from ABEL — DEAD
by **Douglas Arthur Teed** (our narrator)

I arrived to Estero full of solemn and sober purpose. I would get in and out of the garden town with surgical precision, leaving with what I had come for: my father's remains. I intended to take him away from that mad settlement in the Florida wilderness—a town in which the inhabitants had treated him as a messiah—and I would put him to rest in the closest site of respectability, a graveyard off Tampa Bay. Nothing would sway me from that course. I had turned off my human impulse— that sensitivity that drives me toward painting—and in lacking this I had become a sort of automaton. I would remove my father from the custody of those lunatics who worshipped him, and I had little concern for any harm that might be done.

It was with this cultivated cold-heartedness that I entered the town, arriving by night like a villain. I tied my motorised boat to the river landing and paced inland without stopping. To look around myself would have been to acknowledge the crocuses in the flowerbeds, the lion-headed water fountains, the finely crafted footbridges over the drainage canals, all pretty features that might have thawed my numb resolve, so instead I kept my gaze steadfast and in front, unseeing almost. That resolve wilted, however, upon reaching the bathroom of Founder's House. My God, how it wilted.

I had been on the second floor landing only moments before, arguing with two Unity members standing guard. My intention was to depart Estero as rapidly as I had arrived, my father's corpse in tow, and I told the pair as much. They were both women, as were most of the Koreshan Unity. 'Where is he?' I said to them. 'Is he in there?'

One of the women shrunk into the shadows, but the other nodded and stepped in front of the oak door protectively.

'In the damned bathroom,' I said, raving somewhat, I admit. 'Two days he's been festering, and in this humidity. What are you fools thinking by putting him in there?'

'Preservation,' the woman said, 'by means of immersion.'

The phrase chimed of Ulysses Morrow and the dubious Eclectic Medicine he and my father had championed all their lives.

'Let me in,' I said.

She refused flatly.

There was a look that many of the Koreshan women possessed: glowing cheeks, clear eyes, taut arms from working in the fields and orchards. It was this that had given rise to my father's reputation as a corruptor, a hypnotist who lured handsome young women from their husbands. When looking at the Koreshan women up close, however, this impression of youth tended to falter. Worry lines would manifest, liver spots appeared. Not with this woman in front of me. Her fair hair was untouched by greyness and her youth indisputable. As was her stubbornness. She wasn't going to waver from the door, so I shifted her physically and took the handle in my grip—only to find it locked.

'You can either let me in,' I said, 'or I can have Marshal Sanchez of Fort Myers come here and force the matter.' This was no idle threat.

I had been to see the Marshal, and he had practically salivated at the prospect of causing a ruckus in Estero.

'Is that really what you want?' I said. 'A brawl on the porch of this building, now of all times.'

The second woman reappeared from the shadows. 'Ada, maybe you should do as he says?'

'Shut up,' the younger woman said, 'and go wake Richard.'

I put an arm out and swore to the two women that if they brought that degenerate Richard Jentch to this landing then I *would* have the Marshal come, as well as the Fort Myers Press and anyone in Lee County harbouring malice for the Koreshan Unity.

'All right, all right,' the younger woman said, grimacing and shaking her head. 'I'll let you in, but you can't take Koresh's body away. Not now when we are so close to the third day.'

I didn't need to ask what it was the third day signified. I'd heard it enough times that the absurdity barely registered anymore. 'You truly subscribe to all that?' I said.

'I do,' she answered.

'A resurrection is on the cards, then?'

'Yes sir, the conditions are propitious—'

'Bah,' I said. 'You're all damned fools, worse fools than even my father was.'

I reached up to the crest of the thick doorframe. I'd seen the older woman glancing there several times, and sure enough I came upon a bronze key. Without ceremony, I pressed inside and shut the pair out behind me. This was when matters changed.

The bathroom was a plain space with a furnace, a shaving mirror, and a window allowing in just enough moonlight to illuminate it all. In the middle of the warped wooden floor was a copper bathtub; naturally—or unnaturally, as it now occurs to me—I was drawn to that centrepiece.

After two steps it had become apparent form the rippling light that the bathtub was full to the brim. After another step, a smell of salt and spirits reached my nose. One more step and I was on the verge of the tub, peering into it, all my determination dissolving in an instant—for looking up at me from its depths was my father, Cyrus Reed Teed, *Koresh*.

His eyes were open but they had rolled back so only the whites were visible. His mouth was agape too, his tongue and gums paled to the same colour as his slack cheeks. He was dressed, at least. Stoic grey waistcoat, cravat tied deathly tight, pocket watch wrapped round him in a Double-Albert chain. As a priest has his vestments, these were my father's, and not even in death would he be separated from them. And yet the clothes offered only a token dignity. In order to submerge him completely, the Koreshans had bent his knees and twisted his neck gracelessly. His fingers might have been laced at one point, but they had fallen loose now into two stiff-looking claws.

The door opened behind me. The young woman from outside, Ada, approached. Her tone was pleading, as if attempting to quell a quarrel before it could begin. The water was from the river, she explained, and the smell was from the salt and iodine they had added, 'a concoction designed by Koresh himself in his last days. River water for nourishment of the brain, salt to sustain the body, iodine to ward off gangrenous infection.'

There was sympathy in her tone, too. She seemed to acknowledge herself the inanity of this whole display, but she insisted, still, that my father's body must not be moved. When I wrenched my eyes from the corpse I saw that Ada was near tears. 'The third day is looming,' she said, 'more depends on it than you could ever know.

My next words came of their own volition. They weren't premeditated. Rather, they were spoken like words in a dream. Since setting eyes on my father I'd been possessed by pity—for him and his delusions, for his duped followers, for Estero and the whole damned enterprise—and so possessed that my body reacted of its own accord.

'You can have your third day,' I said. Then, shaking my head and reclaiming my senses, 'But not one second more.'

This addition didn't matter. Ada sighed, relieved, and led me downstairs to my father's living quarters, a lush apartment filled with carpets and drapes, and presided over, from atop the bookcase, by a bust of Napoleon. She offered me blankets and pillows enough to smother me, even though I assured her I wouldn't be sleeping. In truth, however, tiredness *had* swept over me, and a low chaise longue was beckoning. Ada left, and I retired to the chair a minute later. A minute after that I was drowning in dreams.

*   *   *

Morning came and brought with it the heat. It was December, true, but that means nothing so far south. I've known Rome in July, Cairo mid-sirocco, Bombay at its most airless, but there's no heat as debilitating as Florida heat. The rugs and finery in my father's quarters promoted the warmth, locking it in and making it heavy. There was no staying there. I got up from the chaise longue and exited by the doorway, which emerged directly onto the sun-soaked porch of Founder's House.

It would have been nice to stand there for a few minutes and enjoy Estero for what modest pleasures it offered. There is something inherently revitalising about looking at palm trees, and the Koreshan orchards imbued the air with a dozen different scents, each distinctive enough to identify if you had the nose for it: lemon, sugar apple, gooseberry, fig. There was plenty to admire in the work ethic of the Koreshans too. They may have just lost their messiah, but you would find no wailing or self-flagellation here. In the vicinity of Founder's House alone, I could see workers tending to the gardens, others ferrying wheelbarrows of sweet potato, and in the shade of the building a group of children were being schooled.

I didn't get a chance to appreciate this, however. All I had was a moment to myself, and in that time I reflected only on the fact that Estero would be gone soon, all the good aspects of it at least—the industriousness, the vigour. My father had promised a resurrection, and when the followers came to understand the extent to which they had been hoodwinked they would flounder. Those who could leave would, back to their families and parishes. Others would stay, for they knew nothing else, but they wouldn't be part of anything. Whether the members realised it or not, the Koreshan Unity had died with my father.

And it was on this dour note my reflections were interrupted by a rough grasp upon my shoulder. I turned and looked into a pair of wild eyes, too close. I didn't recognise their owner. 'Douglas?' he said. 'Koresh's son?'

I nodded, and pulled myself free of the wiry grip. The man was in work trousers much too big for him, only his braces protecting his modesty. He had abandoned a wheelbarrow at the bottom of the porch and I gestured to the fact it was about to tip on its side.

'Forget the barrow,' he said. 'I know why you're here. To take Koresh away. Do it.'

I backed off and raised my hands. 'That's business I'd rather not be discussing.'

The man hummed and gripped one of the posts of the porch. He shook it so hard even roof above swayed. 'You're not listening to me. We both think the same, Douglas. We both *know*. Koresh's body isn't going to come back to life. That's not how it works. Koresh adopts a new body. He enters a fresh vessel. Up there,' he pointed vaguely toward the bathroom upstairs, 'that's just rotting meat.'

The wheelbarrow had tipped now, so I pointed and tried to tell the man he should lift it. He seized my raised finger. 'That's what the others don't understand, Douglas. They think that body *is* Koresh. They think he has to rise in that form—and they think it so badly that they're going to *make* him rise in that form.'

Someone shouted from behind, and I felt relieved to hear steps running to my aid. But first, the man pulled himself close and put his moist mouth to my ear.

'Edison's been here,' he said, 'and he's built them a machine. They're going to zap Koresh's corpse with electro-power and pump him full of dogs' blood. They're going to make him rise, Douglas. They're going to *make* him—'

The man loosed my forefinger as another figure hoisted him away by the underarms. This second man thrust the savage-eyed first in the direction of the porch steps, and kicked him, for good measure, on the seat of his ill-fitting trousers. 'You're testing me, Edgar,' said my liberator. 'If it weren't such a hallowed week I'd beat you till bone showed.'

The man scurried off then, collecting the contents of his wheelbarrow and heading westward toward the Dining Hall. Satisfied, the second man turned and regarded me face on—and I found myself staring at the knobbed nose and spit-straightened fringe of Richard Jentch.

Mongrel, I almost said aloud, before catching myself.

Jentch drew a cigar from inside his jacket and struck a match upon the building's pine siding. 'Forgive Edgar,' he said as he lit. 'His grief is understandable, if misplaced. Koresh is our life and livelihood, and no one knows how to act during this peculiar interlude. No matter. It will be over soon.' He blessed himself, and then regarded me with narrow eyes. 'Why so quiet, Douglas? You look as if you've seen a ghost.'

'A devil,' I said, 'perhaps.'

'Oh, very coy. Very dry indeed.' The cigar tip had blackened but refused to light. Rather than try again, Jentch pocketed it and shook his head. 'You seem to have gotten this idea of me as a rogue. It's unfair, Douglas. Koresh trusted me. He made me an Arch-Triumphant, and I got there on merit.'

'Your merits are another man's criminal charges,' I said. 'I remember you when you first arrived to Estero. Drunken, thuggish, no motive beyond trying to get handsy with the women.'

'And I'm a celibate man now—'

'But you're still a drunken thug. My father knew that and he used you for it. You were his bulldog, Jentch, and from what I've read in the papers you're lucky only to have been jailed once.'

'Oho,' Jentch spun away, and turned back with the bearing of a pugilist. 'You want to talk criminality, Douglas? What about suing your own father on his deathbed? Stealing the money that everyone here donated to him.'

I absorbed this without reaction. 'I sued no one, Jentch. An out of court settlement was made.'

'The actions of a snide thief,' he returned.

'An acknowledgement of fees owed—'

'A knife in Koresh's heart.'

This, I admit, I absorbed less successfully. 'You want to strike me?' I said. 'Fine then. Let's see if those meat hooks are worthy of their Arch-Triumphant status.'

Jentch reared over me with his left fist drawn back, his neck and shoulders so tensed they trembled. I instantly regretted my proposition, but I made sure not to flinch. The moment passed, however, and Jentch lowered his arm. A chestful of air gushed from his flared nostrils. I tried to step around him, but he had penned me into the porch, and he was quite intentionally making it difficult for me get passed. 'Mongrel,' I thought again, and this time I saw no reason to refrain from speaking it aloud.

It was this, I suppose, that prompted Jentch to action once more, and a moment after speaking I came down heavily upon my hands and knees and met the porch forehead first.

I sprawled for a second, but I found my feet again with speed, if not grace. I expected a follow-up assault from Jentch, but the jackal hadn't moved or even turned to face me. I'd be lying if I said I didn't consider launching upon him in that instant, clouting him from behind while I had the chance—but instead I turned on my heels and blasted back to the interior of Founder's House. My mind had set itself on a more potent retaliation.

On the second floor landing I found Ada still standing guard. She had been there all night evidently, and it had added years to her, those greys and liver spots no longer as unimaginable as they had been.

'I'll be taking my father now,' I said to her. An air of sanctimony made into my tone despite my best attempts to stifle it.

'You … I …' The poor girl wasn't wholly awake, but her senses rallied back to her all at once. 'Why?' she exclaimed. 'The third day has barely begun. It's not even the afternoon yet.'

I ignored her protests and decided to say my own piece, something I had been rehearsing, inwardly, just that morning whilst prone on the chaise longue:

'I have no understanding of what it is,' I said, 'that's drawn so many of you women into my father's fanciful web. But you can extricate yourselves now, freely. And you ought to be the first, Ada. It's too late for most of the others. They're damaged, aged, poisoned by Koreshanity. My father has ruined those women, don't be so foolish to deny that. Please, there's no reason for the same to happen to you. Leave Estero, and quick. If you've abandoned a husband then return to him. If you are unwed then you will have no lack of suitors. Will you leave? Tell me you will leave.'

Ada looked up at me, or rather, through me. 'You have no fucking idea why I am here.'

I blinked, and blinked again. Remembering my anger for Jentch, and finding it oddly augmented, I grasped above the doorframe wildly. There was nothing there. 'Give me the key,' I said, unworried now about a sanctimonious tone.

Ada shrugged. 'The door's not locked.'

I thumbed my nose and surged into the stark bathroom. I would drag the corpse through the town on my own if I had to. I would wrap him in a sheet, or maybe I wouldn't. And I would keep my avuncular advice to myself. The Koreshan followers could stay in the Florida wilderness until they mouldered and died if that was what they desired, but they wouldn't have my father. They wouldn't have that.

I was acting as though possessed again, but the instinct driving it had changed. Pity was gone. Something more abstract had taken me. When I think of pity I think of solid things, desolate landscapes, empty marketplaces, sad objects that I can visualise and paint. Thinking of this other abstract emotion conjures only emptiness in my mind—and with emptiness it was met.

How long, I wonder, did I spend staring into that vacant bathtub, the water there but the body gone? And how long afterward did I rave at Ada, threatening her with the full force of the law if she didn't return to me my father's remains? While she, equally astonished, equally raving, declared that a resurrection had taken place and that the time of the great Koreshan revolution was near. Koresh had transcended in form, she said, and his return to Estero was imminent. How long, if at all, did my staggered self lend weight to any of her claims?

I'm incapable of answering these questions with exactitude. In truth, my memory only regains clarity upon leaving Founder's House.

A fog of Koreshans pushed past me on the porch. The word had spread and they left their work to marvel over the bathtub in all its unoccupied splendour. I, meanwhile, was pacing away from the house like a juggernaut, intent that I should get Marshal Sanchez here before the day was out.

This ambition died upon reaching the river landing. I came to a halt when I discerned a lone figure bent over by the tying post; I watched without word as he heaved my motor boat out into the current, the vessel spiralling out of reach and drifting away unmanned.

The figure stared at his good work from the landing and nodded, checking his pocket watch and tucking it away again. There was an unmistakable chemical reek in the air. Water dripped from the man's soaked waistcoat, and his cravat had slipped loose from his high collar.

He twitched when he realised he was being watched. Then he turned and stared at me with wild, hostile eyes.

Baucis and Philemon

Metamorphoses VIII. 611-678

Nathan Murtagh

I'll reach down the bacon pot
if you stoke the ashes and sweep away
the dust of the evening.

When I offer them the goose
and try to chase it around the garden,
I know they will grin at each other
and refuse. They will know then who we are.

And then it will be our turn to look
and know - know that yes, we will be trees
- an oak and a linden, breathing.

Pipes

Metamorphoses I, 689-711

Nathan Murtagh

I would carve you out of wood,
plane you smooth, work
finger holes into your body,
blow away the curls of dust.

Your sound would not be
the hollow whisper of a river reed
or the shrill of a penny whistle.
Your sound would make Pan blush

amongst his flock. He would moan
and glare at the flute he had wrought.

'Plug up their ears.'

Isaiah 6:6-10

Nathan Murtagh

It's that moment when you know you must rise
and cross the cold linoleum to address the trundle
trundle of the dryer at 2 am because its gurning
will – you know this now – keep you grinding your teeth.

You had convinced yourself you could ignore it
- look at you, you are a god amongst appliances! -
but it drones on, hopping now against the stone tiles
of the kitchen floor.

It is the black, spitting mouth of the prophet
who did not flinch or scream at the slap
of coal to his face and chest.
He continues to hop in the kitchen.

Pollock

Nathan Murtagh

When on the line, pollock will thrash
and rave, regardless of size or weight.

When finally quiesced, observe its fading
opaline quality and place in ice

with the others you will have discarded
in the hope of trout.

When packing up, search the ice again
for that fish that will have faded least.

September the first, 1997.

Nathan Murtagh

I remember shading in the blonde of her hair
the day after the accident took place.
I also drew an ambulance crew
and the paparazzi on their bikes.

The day after the accident took place,
I didn't understand what the issue was or why
the paparazzi on their bikes were such a problem.
Sometimes you just want a good picture.

I didn't understand what the issue was or why
people were crying in the streets. I just knew that
sometimes you just want a good picture,
so I did what I was told in the classroom.

People were crying in the streets; I just know that
because we saw them on the TV,
so I did what I was told in the classroom
and put them into the picture.

Because we saw them on the TV
I also drew an ambulance crew
and put them into the picture.
I remember shading in the blonde of her hair.

La Tricolore: Crayola Reflex Blue, Safe, Red 032

Nathan Murtagh

They tell me in their droves to keep a journal,
to write out how it 'makes me feel',
like how putting colours on a page has ruined me
made me feel like the kernel
under the turntable in the microwave after movie night,
how everywhere I look I see Sandstorm #ECD5-40
SpiroDiscoBall #0FC0FC, Red #C91111 [Sporty],
how with every whir of an alarm or flash of blue light
I am back there, fingers pudged against another #[description].
    I am terrified of Frank Spencer.
Some mothers may indeed have them, but I must censor
him and any namesakes, whether imaginary or non-fiction
and I know that it's wrong and it was just a picture
or at least the makings of a picture, but I can taste
the feeling of grief and it tastes like the paste
used to fix this juvenile *Ophelia* to the classroom, this harbinger
of a decade spent filling this bastard journal.
I'll write again tomorrow.

A Brief Delay

Terry McCartan

A Ten Minute Play

◄ **Cast of Characters** ►

SEAN	Early 20s
KARLA	Early 20s
ANNIE	Mid 30s

Airport waiting area. SEAN and KARLA sit in silence. Annie approaches, gives the pair a smile.

ANNIE   Hi.

KARLA   Hi.

Pause.

ANNIE   Off anywhere nice?

SEAN   No.

KARLA   London. We're going to London.

ANNIE   Oh me too.

Pause.

ANNIE   The girls at the desk said the fog should lift
               soon enough.

SEAN   Probably lies.

ANNIE   Sorry?

KARLA   Sean –

SEAN   I said she was probably lying.

ANNIE	What makes you say that?
SEAN:	So no one would kick up a fuss.

Pause.

ANNIE	Anything nice in London?
KARLA	Sorry?
ANNIE	Are you heading over to London for anything nice?
SEAN	We –
KARLA	Just a long weekend. Though we'd make the most of it.
ANNIE	Lovely. That's nice. I'd love a long weekend. I'm back and forward a few times every month for work. It's a pain in the rear, but you have to go where the money is, don't you?
KARLA	Yeah…

Pause.

ANNIE	I'm Annie by the way.
KARLA	Karla. This is Sean.
SEAN	What?

ANNIE	Annie. Pleased to meet you.
SEAN	Yeah.
ANNIE	Sorry, I'm just a bit of a chatterbox.
KARLA	It's fine.
ANNIE	You can tell me to shut up if you want. I just think it makes waiting about go so much faster if you have someone to talk to. I was in here, ages back now, but we got grounded, again –
SEAN	Was the fog just about to lift then too?
KARLA	Sean –
ANNIE	Sorry?
SEAN	The fog. Did they lie to you about the fog then too?
KARLA	You're being rude.
ANNIE	No, it was something with one of the engines I think.
KARLA	Sorry.
ANNIE	It's fine. But, oh what was I saying, god I'm such a scatterbrain.
KARLA	You were grounded.

ANNIE	Yes! We'd been grounded because of the engine or something. Anyway, I got chatting to this old couple who were on the same flight as me. Oh they were lovely, told me about their grandchildren, where they'd been earlier that year, just such wonderful people. And if we hadn't been grounded I'd never have got speaking to them. They'd been married for something like 52 years. Can you imagine that?
SEAN	Yeah, I can.
KARLA	That's crazy.
ANNIE	The man, Christopher I think his name was, told me they'd been courting, courting – I mean, this is how old school this guy was, said they'd been courting since they were 16.
SEAN	Why were they going to London?
ANNIE	To look at the roses in Regent's park.
SEAN	Roses?
KARLA	That's nice.
SEAN	There's roses round by ours.
KARLA	Where?
SEAN	You've seen them.
KARLA	No I haven't.

SEAN	Out the back, near the fence.
KARLA	I don't think so.
SEAN	They're there Karla. Out the back.
KARLA	I didn't notice them.
SEAN	There's only a few but you're bound to have seen them.
KARLA	I haven't.
ANNIE	I love roses. Lilies are my favourite, but it's hard to find wild one. Roses can pop up most places.
SEAN	Why are you going to London again?
ANNIE	Business.
SEAN	Business?
ANNIE	Advertising. They tell you the money's good, they're lying. Have you been before?
SEAN	No. I don't imagine I'll be back.
ANNIE	Oh don't say that. You might like it.
SEAN	Doubt it.
KARLA	Sean.
ANNIE	Travels always good, broadens the mind, isn't that what they say?

Long pause.

ANNIE   Sorry, I'm a mouthpiece. Just makes it go
                         quicker...

Pause.

ANNIE   Think I might just nip to the toilet. Anybody
                         want anything?

The pair look at her awkwardly for a moment.

SEAN   Sorry?

ANNIE   I was joking... Anybody want-... No? Okay...

ANNIE leaves. Pause.

SEAN   Karla.

KARLA   What? What now?

SEAN   Are you seriously going to ignore this?

KARLA   Ignore what?

SEAN   Everything, the fog, her talking about roses

KARLA	Roses?
SEAN	Let's just go home.
KARLA	Don't be stupid. We can't go home.
SEAN	Why?
KARLA	Because. It's booked, it's paid for.
SEAN	I fucking know it's paid for! I had to maxed out my overdraft.
KARLA	Do you want me to get a receipt? Do you want reimbursed?
SEAN	You know I don't give a shit about the money.
KARLA	Then what are you on about?
SEAN	I just want to talk for a minute.
KARLA	It's happening Sean.
SEAN	And that's it?
KARLA	We've talked about it.
SEAN	No we haven't! You've talked about it. You've talked about what's best for you, what you think, what you want!
KARLA	Stop making a scene.
SEAN	I'm not making a scene. I'm talking about what the fuck is going on.

KARLA	Sean, lower your voice.
SEAN	The past two days you haven't stopped long enough for me to get a word in.
KARLA	I had a lot to do.
SEAN	I know. I'd a really good view from the side lines.
KARLA	What's that supposed to mean?
SEAN	Have you even considered the fact that this is happening to me too?
KARLA	Is it? Sorry, last time I checked the appointment's booked under my name.
SEAN	You don't give a fuck, do you?
KARLA	I'm keeping a clear head Sean. I need to do this.
SEAN	Karla, you told me you were pregnant and you were getting an abortion in the same fucking breath.
KARLA	And what?
SEAN	You haven't even thought about what I want.
KARLA	It's my body Sean. If you don't want to be here, go home. I'll do it alone.
SEAN	If you'd just think –

KARLA	Do you want to know what I think? I think it would be stupid to saddle myself with a baby at 22. I think that I'm not ready for this, and neither are you. I think that this is the only option we have. And if you don't like it I think you should shut the fuck up!
SEAN	Karla –
KARLA	Enough! Sean! It's done. We're going over.

Pause.

SEAN	I told my boss my uncle died.
KARLA	What?
SEAN	To get the weekend off. I told him my uncle died.
KARLA	Did he believe you?
SEAN	Told my mum I was going to see friends from uni.
KARLA	Right.
SEAN	What did you say?
KARLA	I told Dad we were going away for the weekend.
SEAN	Why can't we just talk about it?

KARLA	Do you seriously want to have that conversation with your mum or dad? You think I give a shit that you had to lie to your boss?
SEAN	So after this weekend that's it all over?
KARLA	Look, I didn't ask you to come.
SEAN	I'm well aware of that Karla. You could have at least booked two fucking tickets. Having to practically fucking beg you to tell me which flight it was so I could tag along.
KARLA	I didn't think you'd want to go.
SEAN	Of course I don't want to go. I don't want any of this. But you wouldn't know that because, as usual, you're doing your own thing.
KARL	You know what I mean.
SEAN	No, I really don't! I'm trying here, I'm really fucking trying Karla, but you're a closed book. You told me you were getting rid of it like it was such a normal thing, like you were asking me if I wanted a cup of tea.
KARLA	Sean, can we stop?
SEAN	No. we can't. I've been running after you for the past two days and you haven't said a word, except to shut me up.
KARLA	I'm scared Sean. There, is that what you want to hear?

SEAN	I know you are.
KARLA	No, you don't. You think you do, you can imagine if you were in my shoes, but you're not. You have no idea how scared I am. So don't sit there and think that I'm some stone faced bitch, who's acting like she's going to get her fucking nails done. Because I am terrified right now.
SEAN	You don't have to be.
KARLA	Well I am. I'm fucking shitting myself and you're sitting there nagging me, poking about me like I'm some stroppy brat.
SEAN	I'm sorry.
KARLA	You should be.
SEAN	Why can't we give it a go?
KARLA	No Sean.
SEAN	I mean it. We could do it, I'm not saying it wouldn't be hard, I know that, but why can't we make a go at it?
KARLA	Having a baby is not something you 'make a go' at. You need to be ready, we're not. You need to want it, we don't.
SEAN	Who says we don't?

KARLA   I do Sean, I'm telling you now, I don't want
             this. I'm scared, but I still don't want this.

SEAN   What about what I want?

KARLA   I don't care what you want right now Sean. I'm
             sorry, but I can't care right now. And if you've
             something to say, say it to someone else. I'm
             not going to be talked out of this. I'm done.

Pause.
ANNIE comes back over.

ANNIE   The guy at the desk said it'll be soon enough –
             oh sorry.

KARLA   It's fine. We're done talking.

SEAN   Yeah, we're not allowed to talk.

KARLA   Sean...

Pause.

SEAN   Annie, wasn't it?

ANNIE   Yeah.

SEAN   You like to chat to people.

ANNIE   I do. Makes it go quicker.

SEAN	Could I have a chat with you?
ANNIE	Of course you can.
KARLA	Sean…
SEAN	What? I'm just going to have a chat with Annie.
KARLA	Sean –
SEAN	Annie, you're going over for business?
ANNIE	Yes, advertising.
SEAN	And do you see a lot of couples going over?
ANNIE	I suppose, you would yeah. People usually travel in pairs.
SEAN	I'd like to tell you something Annie.
KARLA	Stop it Sean.
SEAN	Karla and I –
KARLA	Sean! This has nothing to do with her.
SEAN	Exactly. It's nothing to do with her! What does it matter if she knows?
KARLA	It's personal Sean.
SEAN	Who's she? What does it matter if Annie knows? You think she cares?
KARLA	We said we wouldn't tell anyone.

SEAN   You said. Your terms, as usual.

KARLA   Sean –

SEAN   Karla and I are going to London for an
                abortion –

KARLA   Sean!

SEAN   That's why we're going to London.

Long pause.

ANNIE   Which clinic?

SEAN   Sorry?

ANNIE   Which clinic are you going to?

KARLA   Bedford Square…

Pause.

ANNIE   They're good there. The staff are- good
                after care…

KARLA   Right…

ANNIE   Yeah…

KARLA   Thanks…

ANNIE	Think it through. I'm not telling you what to do.
KARLA	Okay.
ANNIE	I just chat to people. I'm not judging you, that's not what I'm doing…
SEAN	What are you doing?
ANNIE	It's okay to be scared.
SEAN	You think this is okay then?
ANNIE	I think you have the right to do what you think is for the best, but… it'll follow you.
KARLA	Sorry?
ANNIE	It's not a weekend break. What you're doing, it doesn't last for just a weekend.
KARLA	I know that.
ANNIE	As long as you do. I'm not saying you should or shouldn't. I just like to chat to people.
SEAN	So that's it?
ANNIE	If you do. Take care of yourself after. Properly.
KARLA	I will.
ANNIE	I mean it. The aftercare is just as important.

ANNIE reaches into her bag and produces a card.

ANNIE This might seem a bit strange, but if you feel you can't talk to anyone after, you can give me a call.

ANNIE gives the card to KARLA.

ANNIE I know, I'm just some randomer but, like I said, I like to talk to people.

SEAN She can talk to me, even if she won't, she can.

ANNIE I hope so.

KARLA Thank you.

ANNIE It was nice chatting to you. I hope it goes well for you. Both of you. Whatever happens.

Pause.

ANNIE I think I'd better go.

SEAN I think so too.

ANNIE Bye…

KARLA Bye…

Pause. EXIT ANNIE. The pair sit in silence for a moment. A voice calls over the speakers overhead.

V/O   Calling all passengers for flight EZY830
                        Belfast International to London Gatwick.
                        That's all passengers for flight EZY830 Belfast
                        International to London Gatwick. You are now
                        free to board.

*KARLA sits for a moment. Puts the card in her pocket. She gathers a
hold all and stands to leave. She takes a few steps.*

KARLA   Are you ready?

SEAN   No.

KARLA   Sean –

SEAN   When we come home, what happens then?

KARLA   Let's just get there first.

SEAN   What happens then Karla?

KARLA   I don't know… We tell everyone that we had a
                        nice weekend away…

SEAN   And you're okay with that?

KARLA   Are you coming?

SEAN   Yeah…

Lights fade.

Author Profiles

Elizabeth Byrne was an award-winning BBC producer and director until she made the leap to writing two years ago. She began with an MA in Creative Writing at the Seamus Heaney Centre at Queen's University. Elizabeth writes speculative fiction based on scientific and historical research. Her YA short story 'Vientiane' was published in the For Book's Sake 'RE-Sisters' anthology of new women writers (2016), and her story 'Finding Home' will be in the upcoming (2017) Liberties Press anthology on Irish migration. Elizabeth is working on her first novel, and is about to begin a Northern Bridge Award PhD at Queen's.

Elizabeth Byrne

Brian Wilson is from Newtownards, Northern Ireland. In 2013 he graduated Queen's University with a BA in English Literature and in 2014 he completed an MA in Creative Writing. After the MA he began freelance writing for various websites, exploring the innumerable facets of pop culture. His fiction is literary by nature and enamoured with magical realism. He's currently working on a novel that combines these elements with his love of cinema.

Brian Wilson

E leanor Ford was born in Oxfordshire in 1992 and brought up in Shropshire. She studied English at the University of Leeds before moving to Belfast in 2014 where she completed an MA in Poetry at the Seamus Heaney Centre. In 2015 she read as part of the Linen Hall Writers' Forum reading series and at the John Hewitt International Summer School with The Lifeboat, who produced a pamphlet of her work. Her poems have also appeared in *Poetry and Audience*. Recently she has focused on assembling lyric, text and photography to rework tales from her own family history.

Eleanor Ford

T ara West is called 'a true original' by Glenn Patterson. She completed her MA in Creative Writing in 2013. Her first novel, *Fodder*, was published by Blackstaff Press, and her second novel, *Poets Are Eaten as a Delicacy in Japan*, was published by Liberties Press and described by Ian Sansom as 'the funniest book written by a Northern Irish author this century'. 2016 sees the publication of her memoir of depression and recovery, *Happy Dark,* by Liberties Press, and the inclusion of a short story in New Island's *The Glass Shore*, a high profile anthology of Northern Irish women writers.

Tara West

Noel Russell writes screenplays, TV and radio dramas, fiction and non-fiction, and produces and scripts television programmes. He was a reporter with the *Belfast Telegraph* and news editor of the *Irish News*, produced 20 films for BBCNI's *Spotlight* programme, and set up their *Let's Talk* strand. Educated at QUB and the University of Michigan, he was Editor, General Programmes with BBC Radio Ulster, responsible for the station's arts output. His radio comedy *Blue Skies* was also piloted by BBC Radio Ulster. He is finishing a historical novel and producing an Irish language history programme for BBC Northern Ireland.

Noel Russell

Joanne Higgins was born in 1982 in County Donegal. As an undergraduate, she studied English Literature and History at NUI, Galway. She has worked as a teacher since 2003. Joanne graduated in 2015 from the MA in Creative Writing at Queens University Belfast. She writes stories that feel 'real' to her about everyday lives. She is moved to the page in defense of the forgotten: neglected children, delinquent teens, old people in nursing home windows, even dead rats on the road. She is currently working on her first novel set in contemporary Donegal, but has threatened to write a historical novel.

Joanne Higgins

K erri Ward is from Dublin and has a bachelor's degree in English Literature and Drama in Trinity College, Dublin. After graduating from the MA programme in 2014 she embarked on a career in publishing and now works as an editor on educational children's books. She has a strong background in children's fiction and is currently working on a chapter book for 7 to 10 year olds, in addition to an experimental novel for adults.

Kerri Ward

E mma Devlin is a graduate of Queen's University Belfast, where she received a BA in English and French, and an MA in Creative Writing. She is an aspiring librarian with an interest in writing short, literary fiction, particularly historical fiction. She currently lives in Bangor.

Emma Devlin

Peter Alexander Arden works part-time, enjoys a variety of physical activity, and self-identifies as a human male. He writes because it was his dream job as a child, and, despite the trouble he has stringing sentences together, he is way too stubborn to give up this dream. A recent MA Creative Writing student at Queen's, writing mainly realistic fiction, Peter is busy putting the final touches on the first part of a series set in Northern Ireland, entitled *Trigger Warning*, which he intends to publish as soon as someone lets him.

Peter McLoughlin

For contact, e-mail: alexanderarden@outlook.com

Emily S Cooper is a poet from Derry. She studied at Goldsmiths College, Glasgow University and most recently Queen's where she received a Masters in Poetry. Her work has been published in the *Honest Ulsterman, Belleville Park Pages* and the *Connections* Anthology. Her poetry deals with experiences of being home and away, she is currently in a cafe in Athens.

Emily S. Cooper

Andrew Maguire was born and lives in Omagh, County Tyrone. He was educated at the Christian Brothers and Queen's University Belfast, graduating with a degree in English and Creative Writing and an MA in Creative Writing. His main interest is in prose and drama, as vehicles for portraying universal, relatable experiences. He is currently employed at South West College, which involves writing and editing the college blog, *'Way Out West'*. Andrew is an active member of the committee for the annual Benedict Kiely Literary Festival.

Andrew Maguire

Joseph Robinson was born in 1990 and lives in Muskegon, Michigan. He received his MA in Creative Writing from Queen's University Belfast in 2015.

Fueled by coffee, nicotine, and quiet existential rage; Joseph's work is character driven and often set in the American landscape of his youth. He values simple language and complex themes; stories informed by emotion, guided by structure. He strives to achieve the same in his own work.

Joseph Robinson

Currently, he is in a love-hate relationship with his first attempted novel: a young adult story about gender and identity. 'The Air Marshal' is Joseph's first published work: he hopes you like it.

James Conor Patterson is 27 and from Newry, Co. Down. His work has appeared in *Magma, The Moth, New Welsh Review, New Statesman, Poetry Ireland Review,* and *The Stinging Fly.* In 2015 he read as part of the *Poetry Ireland Introductions* series and in 2013 he received the *iYeats* 'Emerging Talent' Award for poetry. He has been highly commended for the *Patrick Kavanagh Award,* shortlisted for the Bridport Prize and longlisted for the UK National Poetry Award.

James Patterson

Mick Draine is a Belfast playwright. He has 20 years experience in theatre as a technical and production manger. In 2013 his first play *Lemonade sandwich* was produced by Brassneck Theatre Company, which opened in the Grand Opera House Belfast. It went on to sell out two tours across Northern Ireland, finishing at the Lyric Theatre in 2015. Mick produced his second play *The Good Room* as part of the West Belfast Festival in 2016. His writing is muscular, funny, and tender with foul-mouthed street talk. His characters are full of a sense of failure, regret and love.

Mick Draine

Stephen Cunningham was born and raised in Northern Ireland. He holds an MA with distinction in Creative Writing from Queen's University Belfast. Previous publications include *Catching the Bus,* which, out of over 7,000 entrants, won eighth place in the *Writer's Digest* thirteenth annual Short Short Story Competition. In 2015 he was awarded funding for his comedic novel, *What I Knew*, as part of the Arts Council NI's General Art Award Scheme. He currently lives in Belfast.

Stephen Cunningham

Patrick Macfarlane is a qualified lawyer, specialising in financial regulation: the subject of both his pamphlet of poetry, *Show Next* (If A Leaf Falls Press, 2016), and a forthcoming play about the forex scandal. Patrick developed a particular interest in poetic form while studying English at Oxford, and during his master's at the Seamus Heaney Centre. Now embarking on a PhD at Queen's, Patrick plans to examine approaches to work and the work ethic in modern Irish poetry. His creative and critical interests include the transition from hunting to agriculture, work in theology, industrial working culture, automation and unemployment.

Patrick MacFarlane

Jonathan Vischer is a writer of prose fiction. Born in London, I moved to Belfast twenty years ago.

My stories often employ allegory to explore the perceptions of enclosed communities. To this end, he has recently completed a novel, *Bird Rock*: the story of an island people obsessed with the cult of flight. Alongside teaching, he is working for a Creative Writing PhD that involves researching Jacobean prison pamphlets. An interest in the power of belief, in all its conventional and heretical forms and underpins his work

Jonathan Vischer

Kerry Millar has always looked for the whimsy in everything, including the bleaker situations in life, and can never resist injecting this into her writing. Living in the countryside for most of her life, inspiration comes from the dogs barking at the moon and the rabbits scurrying into their burrows. Kerry believes that we share a strong connection with other living creatures, and will often write about the relationships between humans and their non-human companions. She enjoys the quiet, cool season of winter, and believes it hides the most mysteries. To her, snow is the closest thing to real life magic.

Kerry Millar

Damien Laughlin is a twenty-four year old writer from Derry, currently based in Belfast. He graduated from the Queen's Creative Writing MA in 2015 and has since been published in *Penny Mag* and *The Cadaverine Magazine*. His short story 'Boys' was also recently produced by *Pseudopod*, the internet's longest running horror fiction podcast. Damien's writing has touched on an eclectic range of themes and subjects, frequently borrowing from weird fiction and traditional horror to subvert genre norms. He is currently working on a series of short stories and submitting to a variety of magazines and journals.

Damien Laughlin

Nathan Murtagh is a Belfast-based poet and actor, originally from Dublin. He studied for an M.A. in poetry at the Seamus Heaney centre after studying for a B.A. in English and Theology at Queen's University Belfast. His work has been published by *The Lifeboat* as part of its series of readings in Belfast. His recent work deals with translation and the death of Diana Spencer. He lives in Lisburn with his wife Lynsey.

Nathan Murtagh